SONGS
OF
FAITH AND HOPE

EDITED BY

JAMES M. BLACK

FOR THE PUBLISHERS

JENNINGS AND GRAHAM
CINCINNATI
Chicago   Kansas City   San Francisco

EATON AND MAINS
NEW YORK
Boston   Pittsburg   Detroit

PREFACE.

There is no doubt of the welcome of a good song. This is more true of a gospel song. It is most true of a goodly collection of gospel songs. The book which we are introducing with this opening word has two great advantages over many of its kind. In the first place, it is official: issued by the Western Methodist Book Concern, one of the official publishing-houses of our great Church. It may be presumed that great care has been exercised in the selection of its contents, having in mind the proper teaching which the Church should indorse. Second, it is edited by a man well known in the world of gospel songs. A glance at the contents will show his skill and excellent taste. Prof. J. M. Black is the only one of many song writers and composers who was selected as a member of the Joint Commission to produce the official Methodist Hymnal recently published.

The very best talent is brought into use, and we think that without question it is the best collection of the best hymns and tunes intended for revival and social work that has ever been offered to the public. The selections have been made with reference to their usefulness in Church work, and the book is most heartily commended for its adaptation to the prayer-meeting, the Sunday-school, the Young People's Meeting, and the revival service. It is not intended to take the place of the Church Hymnal, but to supplement it in work where a cheaper and lighter book is desired.

H. C. JENNINGS.

SONGS OF FAITH AND HOPE.

✦ ✦ ✦ ✦ ✦

No. 1. I Remember Calvary.

Rev. W. C. Martin.   Jas. M. Black.

1. Where He may lead me I will go, For I have learned to trust Him so,
2. O I de-light in His com-mand, Love to be led by His dear hand,
3. On-ward I go, nor doubt nor fear, Hap-py with Christ, my Sav-iour, near,

And I re-mem-ber 'twas for me, That He was slain on Cal-va-ry.
His di-vine will is sweet to me, Hallowed by blood-stain'd Cal-va-ry.
Trusting that I some day shall see Je-sus, my Friend of Cal-va-ry.

CHORUS.

Je-sus shall lead me night and day, Je-sus shall lead me all the way;

He is the tru-est Friend to me, For I re-mem-ber Cal-va-ry.

No. 2. Help Just a Little.

W. A. SPENCER, D. D.   WM. J. KIRKPATRICK.

1. Broth-er, for Christ's kingdom sighing, Help a lit-tle, help a lit-tle;
2. Is thy cup made sad by tri-al? Help a lit-tle, help a lit-tle;
3. Tho' no wealth to thee is giv-en, Help a lit-tle, help a lit-tle;
4. Let us live for one an-oth-er, Help a lit-tle, help a lit-tle;
5. Tho' thy life is press'd with sorrow, Help a lit-tle, help a lit-tle;

Help to save the mill-ions dy-ing, Help just a lit-tle.
Sweet-en it with self-de-ni-al, Help just a lit-tle.
Sac-ri-fice is gold in heav-en, Help just a lit-tle.
Help to lift each fall-en broth-er, Help just a lit-tle.
Brave-ly look tow'rd God's to-mor-row, Help just a lit-tle.

CHORUS.

O the wrongs that we may righten, O the hearts that we may lighten!

O the skies that we may brighten! Help-ing just a lit-tle.

No. 3. Higher Ground.

Rev. Johnson Oatman, Jr.   Chas. H. Gabriel.

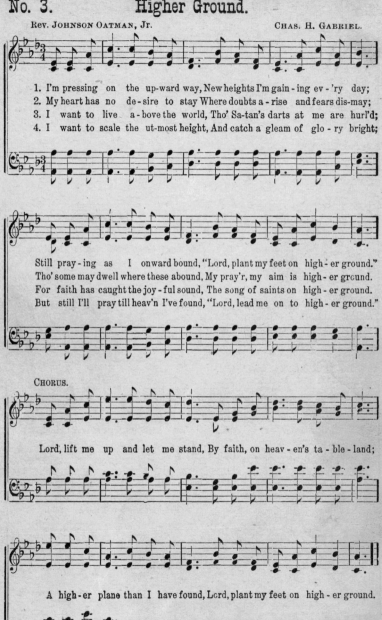

1. I'm pressing on the up-ward way, New heights I'm gain-ing ev-'ry day;
2. My heart has no de-sire to stay Where doubts a-rise and fears dis-may;
3. I want to live a-bove the world, Tho' Sa-tan's darts at me are hurl'd;
4. I want to scale the ut-most height, And catch a gleam of glo-ry bright;

Still pray-ing as I onward bound, "Lord, plant my feet on high-er ground."
Tho' some may dwell where these abound, My pray'r, my aim is high-er ground.
For faith has caught the joy-ful sound, The song of saints on high-er ground.
But still I'll pray till heav'n I've found, "Lord, lead me on to high-er ground."

CHORUS.

Lord, lift me up and let me stand, By faith, on heav-en's ta-ble-land;

A high-er plane than I have found, Lord, plant my feet on high-er ground.

The Half was Never Told.

P. P. B.   P. P. BLISS.

1. Re - peat the sto - ry o'er and o'er, Of *grace* so full and free;
2. Of *peace* I on - ly knew the name, Nor found my soul its rest
3. My high - est place is ly - ing low At my Re-deem-er's feet;
4. And oh, what rapt-ure will it be With all the host a - bove,

I love to hear it more and more, Since grace has res - cued me.
Un - til the sweet-voiced an - gel came To soothe my wea - ry breast.
No re - al *joy* in life I know, But in His serv - ice sweet.
To sing thro' all e - ter - ni - ty The won - ders of His *love*.

CHORUS.
The half . . . was never told,

The half was nev - er told, The half was never told,

never told,   never told,

The half . . . was nev er told.

1. Of grace di-vine, so won-der-ful, The half was nev - er told.
2. Of peace, etc.
3. Of joy, etc.   never told.
4. Of love, etc.

No. 5. Make Me a Blessing To-day.

IDA SCOTT TAYLOR.   W. H. DOANE.

1. O soft - ly the Spir - it is whisp'ring to- me, With ten - der com-
2. Some heart may be long - ing for on - ly a word, Whose love by the
3. Some soul may be plunged in the dark-est de - spair, Whose shad-ows would
4. Come all ye that la - bor, ye wea - ry and worn, Come ye who in

pas - sion, with pit - y - ing plea; I hear His be - seech-ing, and
Spir - it is quick-ened and stirred; Now grant, bless - ed Sav - iour, this
melt in the sun - light of pray'r; O give me, dear Sav - iour, I
sor - row or sin - ful-ness mourn; With me this pe - ti - tion to

earn - est - ly pray That Je - sus will make me a bless-ing to - day.
serv - ice to me, Of speak-ing a com - fort-ing mes-sage for Thee.
hum - bly im - plore, The sweet con - so - la - tion that soul to re-store.
Je - sus con - vey: O make me a bless - ing, dear Sav-iour to - day.

CHORUS.

Lord, make ... me a blessing to-day, A bless-ing to some one, I pray;
Lord, make me a blessing.   I pray;

In all that I do, in all that I say, O make me a blessing to - day.

Does Jesus Care?

REV. FRANK E. GRAEFF.   J. LINCOLN HALL.

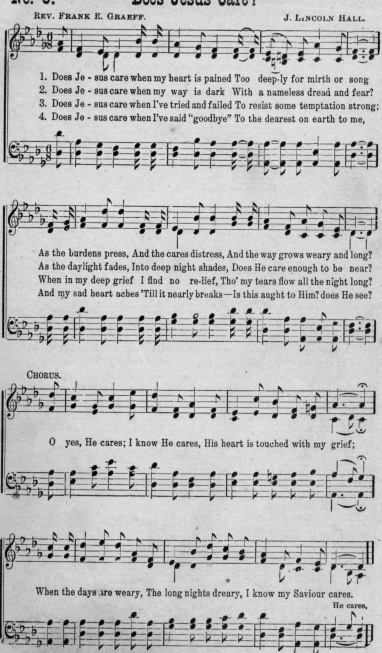

1. Does Je - sus care when my heart is pained Too deep-ly for mirth or song
2. Does Je - sus care when my way is dark With a nameless dread and fear?
3. Does Je - sus care when I've tried and failed To resist some temptation strong;
4. Does Je - sus care when I've said "goodbye" To the dearest on earth to me,

As the burdens press, And the cares distress, And the way grows weary and long?
As the daylight fades, Into deep night shades, Does He care enough to be near?
When in my deep grief I find no re-lief, Tho' my tears flow all the night long?
And my sad heart aches 'Till it nearly breaks—Is this aught to Him? does He see?

CHORUS.

O yes, He cares; I know He cares, His heart is touched with my grief;

When the days are weary, The long nights dreary, I know my Saviour cares.

He cares,

No. 7. I'll Follow Where He Leads.

Lou W. Wilson.

M. C. Williams.

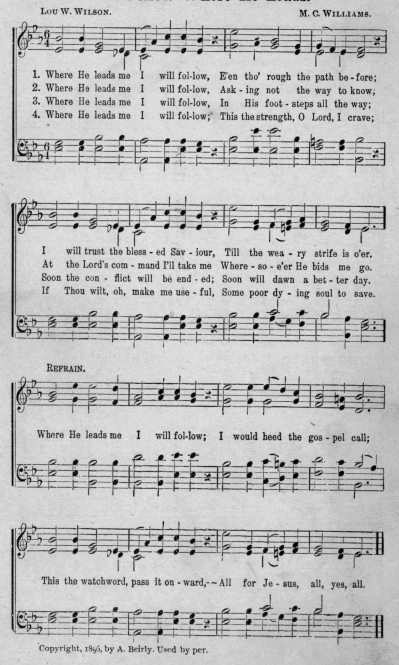

1. Where He leads me I will fol-low, E'en tho' rough the path be-fore;
2. Where He leads me I will fol-low, Ask - ing not the way to know;
3. Where He leads me I will fol-low, In His foot - steps all the way;
4. Where He leads me I will fol-low; This the strength, O Lord, I crave;

I will trust the bless - ed Sav - iour, Till the wea - ry strife is o'er.
At the Lord's com - mand I'll take me Where - so - e'er He bids me go.
Soon the con - flict will be end - ed; Soon will dawn a bet - ter day.
If Thou wilt, oh, make me use - ful, Some poor dy - ing soul to save.

Refrain.

Where He leads me I will fol-low; I would heed the gos - pel call;

This the watchword, pass it on - ward, - ~ All for Je - sus, all, yes, all.

No. 8. I Shall Be Like Him.

W. A. S.   Rev. W. A. Spencer, D. D.

1. When I shall reach the more ex-cel-lent glo-ry, And all my tri-als are passed, I shall be-hold Him, O won-der-ful sto-ry! I shall be like Him at last.

2. We shall not wait till the glo-ri-ous dawn-ing Breaks on the vis-ion so fair, Now we may wel-come the heav-en-ly morning, Now we His im-age may bear.

3. More and more like Him, re-peat the blest sto-ry, O-ver and o-ver a-gain, Changed by His Spir-it from glo-ry to glo-ry, I shall be sat-is-fied then.

CHORUS.

I shall be like Him, I shall be like Him, And in His beau-ty shall shine; I shall be like Him, won-drous-ly like Him, Je-sus my Sav-iour di-vine.

No. 9. My Saviour First of All.

FANNY J. CROSBY.　　　　　　　　　　　　　　　JNO. R. SWENEY.

1. When my life-work is end-ed, and I cross the swell-ing tide, When the
2. Oh, the soul-thrilling rapt-ure when I view His bless-ed face, And the
3. Oh, the dear ones in glo-ry, how they beck-on me to come, And our
4. Thro' the gates to the cit-y in a robe of spot-less white, He will

bright and glorious morning I shall see; I shall know my Re-deemer when I
lus - tre of His kind-ly beam-ing eye; How my full heart will praise Him for the
part-ing at the riv-er I re-call; To the sweet vales of E-den they will
lead me where no tears will ev - er fall; In the glad song of a-ges I shall

reach the oth - er side, And His smile will be the first to wel-come me.
mer - cy, love, and grace, That prepares for me a man-sion in the sky.
sing my welcome home, But I long to meet my Sav-iour first of all.
min - gle with de-light; But I long to meet my Sav-iour first of all.

CHORUS.

I shall know . . Him, I shall know Him, And redeemed by His side I shall stand;
I shall know Him,

I shall know Him, I shall know Him By the print of the nails in His hand.

J. Dear to the Heart of the Shepherd.

Mrs. Mary B. Wingate.

Wm. J. Kirkpatrick.

1. Dear to the heart of the Shep - herd, Dear are the sheep of His fold;
2. Dear to the heart of the Shep - herd, Dear are the lambs of His fold;
3. Dear to the heart of the Shep - herd, Dear are the "ninety and nine."
4. Green are the pastures in - vit - ing, Sweet are the waters and "still;"

Dear is the love that He gives them, Dear-er than sil - ver or gold.
Some from the pastures are stray - ing, Hungry and helpless and cold.
Dear are the sheep that have wan - dered Out in the des-ert to pine.
Lord, we will answer Thee glad - ly, "Yes, blessed Master, we will!

Dear to the heart of the Shep - herd, Dear are His "oth-er" lost sheep;
See, the good Shepherd is seek - ing, Seek-ing the lambs that are lost;
Hark! He is ear-nest-ly call - ing, Ten-der-ly plead-ing to - day;
Make us Thy true un - der - shep - herds, Give us a love that is deep;

O - ver the mountains He fol - lows, O - ver the wa-ters so deep.
Bringing them in with re - joic - ing, Saved at such in - fi - nite cost.
"Will you not seek for my lost ones, Off from my shel-ter a - stray?"
Send us out in - to the des - ert Seek-ing Thy wan-der-ing sheep."

Dear to the Heart.

CHORUS. *poco rit.*

Out in the des-ert they wan - der, Hun-gry and help-less and cold;

f a tempo.

Off to the res-cue He hast - ens, Bringing them back to the fold.
(*4th verse.*) we'll hast - en, Bringing them back to the fold.

No. 11. Hide Thou Me.

FANNY J. CROSBY.   ROBERT LOWRY, D. D.

1. In Thy cleft, O Rock of A - ges, Hide Thou me; When the fit - ful tem-pest
2. From the snare of sin - ful pleasure, Hide Thou me: Thou, my soul's e - ter - nal
3. In the lone - ly night of sor-row; Hide Thou me; Till in glo - ry dawns the

rag - es, Hide Thou me; Where no mor - tal arm can sev - er From my
treas-ure, Hide Thou me; When the world its pow'r is wield-ing, And my
mor-row, Hide Thou 'me; In the sight of Jor-dan's bil - low Let Thy

heart Thy love for - ev - er, Hide me, O Thou Rock of A-ges, Safe in Thee.
heart is al-most yielding, Hide me, O Thou Rock of A-ges, Safe in Thee.
bo - som be my pil-low; Hide me, O Thou Rock of A-ges, Safe in Thee.

No. 12. When the Bridegroom Comes.

E. R. Latta. Alt.　　　　　　　　　　　　　　　Wm. J. Kirkpatrick.

1. Will our lamps be filled and read - y, When the Bridegroom comes? And our
2. Shall we hear a wel-come sounding, When the Bridegroom comes? And a
3. Don't de - lay our prep - a - ra-tion Till the Bridegroom comes; Lest there
4. It may be a time of sor-row When the Bridegroom comes; If our
5. Oh, there'll be a glo-rious meet-ing When the Bridegroom comes; And a

lights be clear and steady, When the Bridegroom comes? In the night,　that sol-emn
shout of joy resounding When the Bridegroom comes? In the night,　that sol-emn
be a sep - a-ra-tion, When the Bridegroom comes. In the night,　that sol-emn
oil we hope to borrow, When the Bridegroom comes. In the night,　that sol-emn
hal - le-lu-jah greeting, When the Bridegroom comes. In the night,　that joy-ful

night, (that solemn night,) Will our lamps be burning bright, When the Bridegroom comes?
night, (that solemn night,) Will our lamps be burning bright, When the Bridegroom comes?
night, (that solemn night,) Will our lamps be burning bright, When the Bridegroom comes?
night, (that solemn night,) Will our lamps be burning bright, When the Bridegroom comes?
night, (that joy-ful night,) With our lamps all burning bright, When the Bridegroom comes.

CHORUS.

{ O be ready! O be ready! O be ready when the Bridegroom comes!
{ O be ready! O be ready! O be ready when the (Omit . . .) Bridegroom comes!

No. 13.   I Know that My Redeemer.

JESSIE BROWN POUNDS.

J. H. FILLMORE.

1. I know that my Re-deem-er liv - eth, And on the earth . . .
2. I know His prom-ise nev - er fail - eth, The word He speaks, . .
3. I know my man-sion He pre - par - eth, That where He is, ...

again shall stand;   I know e - ter-nal life He giv-eth,That grace and
it can-not die;   Tho' cru - el death my flesh as - sail - eth, Yet I shall
there I shall be;   O wondrous tho't, for me He car - eth, And He at

CHORUS.

pow'r . . . . are in His hand.   { I know, I   know . . .
see . . . . Him by and by.   { And on the   earth . . .
last . . . . will come for me.

that Je-sus liv - eth,)
a - gain shall (*Omit.*) } stand; I know, I   know . . . . that life He

rit.

giv - eth, That grace and pow'r . . . are in His hand. . . .
are in His hand;

No. 14. Will there be Any Stars?

E. E. HEWITT.   JNO. R. SWENEY.

1. I am think-ing to-day of that beau-ti-ful land I shall reach when the
2. In the strength of the Lord let me la-bor and pray, Let me watch as a
3. Oh, what joy it will be when His face I be-hold, Liv-ing gems at His

sun go-eth down; When thro' won-der-ful grace by my Sav-iour I stand,
win-ner of souls; That bright stars may be mine in the glo-ri-ous day,
feet to lay down; It would sweeten my bliss in the cit-y of gold,

CHORUS.

Will there be a-ny stars in my crown?
When His praise like the sea-bil-low rolls. Will there be a-ny stars, a-ny
Should there be a-ny stars in my crown.

stars in my crown, When at ev'ning the sun goeth down? When I wake with the
goeth down?

blest in the man-sions of rest, Will there be a-ny stars in my crown?
a-ny stars in my crown?

No. 15. All the Way My Saviour Leads.

F. J. C.

ROBERT LOWRY, D. D.

1. All the way my Sav-iour leads me, What have I to ask be-side?
2. All the way my Sav-iour leads me, Cheers each wind-ing path I tread;
3. All the way my Sav-iour leads me; O the ful-ness of His love!

Can I doubt His ten-der mer-cy, Who thro' life has been my guide?
Gives me grace for ev-'ry tri-al, Feeds me with the liv-ing bread;
Per-fect rest to me is prom-ised In my Fa-ther's house a-bove;

Heav'n-ly peace, di-vin-est com-fort, Here by faith in Him to dwell!
Tho' my wea-ry steps may fal-ter, And my soul a-thirst may be,
When my spir-it, clothed, im-mor-tal, Wings its flight to realms of day,

For I know, what-e'er be-fall me, Je-sus do-eth all things well;
Gush-ing from the Rock be-fore me, Lo! a spring of joy I see;
This my song thro' end-less a-ges—Je-sus led me all the way;

For I know, what-e'er be-fall me, Je-sus do-eth all things well.
Gush-ing from the Rock be-fore me, Lo! a spring of joy I see.
This my song thro' end-less a-ges—Je-sus led me all the way.

No. 16. Sweet Peace, the Gift of God's Love.

P. P. B.

P. P. BILHORN.

1. There comes to my heart one sweet strain, A glad and a joy-ous re - frain,
   sweet strain,   refrain,
2. By Christ on the cross peace was made, My debt by His death was all paid,
   was made,   all paid,
3. When Je - sus as Lord I had crowned, My heart with this peace did abound.
   had crowned,   abound,
4. In   Je - sus for peace I a - bide, And as   I keep close to His side,
   abide,   His side,

I   sing it a - gain and a - gain, Sweet peace, the gift of God's love
No oth - er foun-da-tion is   laid For peace, the gift of God's love.
In Him the rich blessing I found, Sweet peace, the gift of God's love.
There's nothing but peace doth be - tide, Sweet peace, the gift of God's love.

CHORUS.

Peace, peace, sweet peace! Won - der - ful gift from a - bove!   O
                                                         a - bove!

won-der-ful, won - der - ful   peace! Sweet peace, the gift of God's love!

No. 17. Standing on the Promises.

R. K. C.

R. KELSO CARTER.

1. Stand-ing on the prom-is - es of Christ my King, Thro' e - ter - nal
2. Stand-ing on the prom-is - es that can - not fail, When the howl-ing
3. Stand-ing on the prom-is - es, I now can see Per - fect, pres - ent
4. Stand-ing on the prom-is - es of Christ the Lord, Bound to Him e -
5. Stand-ing on the prom-is - es, I can - not fail, List-'ning ev - 'ry

a - ges let His praises ring: Glo - ry in the high-est, I will shout and sing,
storms of doubt and fear as-sail, By the liv - ing Word of God I shall prevail,
cleansing in the blood for me; Stand-ing in the lib - er-ty where Christ makes free,
ter - nal - ly by love's strong chord, O - ver-com - ing dai - ly with the Spirit's sword,
mo - ment to the Spir-it's call, Rest-ing in my Sav-iour, as my all in all,

CHORUS.

Standing on the promises of God. Stand - ing, stand - ing,
Standing on the promises, standing on the promises,

Stand-ing on the prom-is - es of God my Sav-iour; Stand - ing,
Standing on the prom-is - es,

stand - ing, I'm stand-ing on the prom-is - es of God.
stand-ing on the prom-is - es,

No. 18. Drifting Down.

JESSIE BROWN POUNDS.   W. E. M. HACKLEMAN.

Slowly with expression.

1. You are drift-ing far from shore, lean-ing on an i-dle oar, You are
2. Lights up-on the home-land shore give you warn-ing o'er and o'er, You are
3. Voic-es from the home-land shore faint-er grow as they implore, You are

drifting, slowly drifting, drifting down; You are drifting with the tide to the
drifting, slowly drifting, drifting down; Soon be-yond the har-bor bar will your
drifting, slowly drifting, drifting down; O my brother, do not wait, heed them

rit. ad lib.

o-cean wild and wide, You are drift-ing, slow-ly drift-ing, drift-ing down.
boat be car-ried far, You are drift-ing, slow-ly drift-ing, drift-ing down.
ere it be too late, Ere for-ev-er you have drift-ed, drift-ed down.

CHORUS. *rit.*   *a tempo.*   *rit.*   *a tempo.*

You are drift-ing down, drift-ing down To the
You are drift-ing, slow-ly drift-ing, you are slow-ly drift-ing down

rit.   *a tempo.*

dark and awful sea; You are drift-ing down From a Fa-ther's loving care,
You are drifting, slow-ly drift-ing.

Drifting Down.

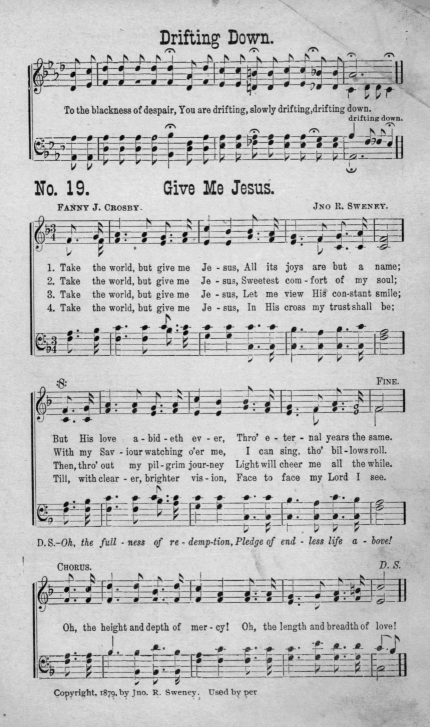

To the blackness of despair, You are drifting, slowly drifting, drifting down.

drifting down.

No. 19. Give Me Jesus.

FANNY J. CROSBY.

JNO R. SWENEY.

1. Take the world, but give me Je - sus, All its joys are but a name;
2. Take the world, but give me Je - sus, Sweetest com - fort of my soul;
3. Take the world, but give me Je - sus, Let me view His con-stant smile;
4. Take the world, but give me Je - sus, In His cross my trust shall be;

FINE.

But His love a - bid - eth ev - er, Thro' e - ter - nal years the same.
With my Sav - iour watching o'er me, I can sing, tho' bil - lows roll.
Then, thro' out my pil - grim jour-ney Light will cheer me all the while.
Till, with clear - er, brighter vis - ion, Face to face my Lord I see.

D.S.—Oh, the full - ness of re - demp-tion, Pledge of end - less life a - bove!

CHORUS.

D. S.

Oh, the height and depth of mer - cy! Oh, the length and breadth of love!

No. 20. Let Jesus Come Into Your Heart.

C. H. M.

Mrs. C. H. MORRIS.

1. If you are tired of the load of your sin, Let Je - sus come in - to your heart; If you de-sire a new life to be - gin,
2. If 'tis for pur - i - ty now that you sigh, Let Je - sus come in - to your heart; Fount - ains for cleansing are flow - ing near by,
3. If there's a tem - pest your voice can - not still, Let Je - sus come in - to your heart; If there's a void this world nev - er can fill,
4. If friends, once trust - ed, have prov - en un - true, Let Je - sus come in - to your heart; Find what a friend He will be un - to you,
5. If you would join the glad songs of the blest, Let Je - sus come in - to your heart; If you would en - ter the man-sions of rest,

Let Je - sus come in - to your heart.

CHORUS.

Just now, your doubt-ings give o'er; Just now, re - ject Him no more; Just now, throw o - pen the door; Let Je - sus come in - to your heart.

No. 21.   Anywhere With Jesus.

JESSIE H. BROWN.   D. B. TOWNER.

1. An - y-where with Je - sus I can safe - ly go,   An - y-where He
2. An - y-where with Je - sus I am not a - lone,   Oth - er friends may
3. An - y-where with Je - sus I can go to sleep,   When the dark'ning

leads me in this world be - low;   An - y-where with-out Him, dear - est
fail me, He is still my own;   Tho' His hands may lead me o - ver
shad-ows round a - bout me creep;   Know-ing I shall wak - en nev - er

joys would fade,   An - y-where with Je - sus I am not a - fraid.
drear-est ways,   An - y-where with Je - sus is a house of praise.
more to roam,   An - y-where with Je - sus will be home, sweet home.

CHORUS.

An - y-where! an - y-where! Fear I can - not know,

An - y-where with Je - sus I can safe - ly go.

No. 22. Open Wide the Door.

W. KITCHING. J. H. BURKE.

1. Je - sus knocks; He calls to thee; "Wea - ry one, O come to me;"
2. Je - sus knocks; He comes to save, 'Twas for thee His life He gave,
3. Je - sus knocks, is knock - ing still; Yield to Him at once Thy will;
4. Je - sus knocks; the mo - ments fly; While sal - va - tion yet is nigh,

He can save, and on - ly He; O - pen wide the door.
He hath tri-umphed o'er the grave; O - pen wide the door.
He with joy thy heart can fill; O - pen wide the door.
Ere the Sav-iour pass - eth by, O - pen wide the door.
O - pen, o - pen wide the door,

CHORUS.

O - pen wide the door,
O - pen, o - pen wide; O - pen wide the door;

O - pen wide the door, He can save, and
O - pen wide, O wide; O - pen wide the door;

on - ly He;— O - pen wide the door.
O - pen; o - pen wide, O - pen wide the door;

No. 23. Glory All the Way!

Rev. J. H. Sammis.   D. B. Towner.

1. Saved by grace a - lone, God's own Word be - liev - ing: It is glo - ry
2. Not a care have I since my Sav - iour car - eth! It is glo - ry
3. Sev - ered from the world His dear name con - fess - ing: It is glo - ry
4. Sin - ner, put your trust in this lov - ing Sav - iour; It is glo - ry
5. Work - ing day by day, mind - ed that He sees us, It is glo - ry

all the way! Walk - ing in the light, dai - ly grace re - ceiv - ing: It is
all the way! Guid - ed by His eye, while with me He far - eth: It is
all the way! Tak - ing up the cross, sharing in the bless - ing: It is
all the way! Free - ly He for - gives all our past be - hav - ior: It is
all the way! Watch and wait and pray, look - ing un - to Je - sus: It is

CHORUS.

glo - ry all the way! Glo - ry! Glo - ry!
Glo - ry all the way, yes, glo - ry all the way!

It is glo - ry all the way! .... Glo - ry!
It is glo - ry, glo - ry all the way! Glo - ry all the way, yes,

Glo - ry! It is glo - ry all the way! ....
Glo - ry all the way, It is glo - ry, glo - ry, glo - ry all the way!

No. 24. Jesus, I Come.

WILLIAM T. SLEEPER. GEORGE C. STEBBINS.

1. Out of my bond-age, sorrow and night, Je-sus, I come, Je-sus, I come;
2. Out of my shame-ful fail-ure and loss, Je-sus, I come, Je-sus, I come;
3. Out of un-rest and ar-ro-gant pride, Je-sus, I come, Je-sus, I come;
4. Out of the fear and dread of the tomb, Je-sus, I come, Je-sus, I come:

In-to Thy free-dom glad-ness and light, Je-sus, I come to Thee;
In-to the glo-rious gain of Thy cross, Je-sus, I come to Thee;
In-to Thy bless-ed wlll to a-bide, Je-sus, I come to Thee:
In-to the joy and light of my home Je-sus, I come to Thee;

Out of my sick-ness in-to Thy health, Out of my want and in-to Thy wealth,
Out of earth's sorrows in-to Thy balm, Out of life's storms and in-to Thy calm,
Out of my-self to dwell in Thy love, Out of des-pair in-to raptures a-bove,
Out of the depths of ru-in un-told, In-to the peace of Thy sheltering fold,

Out of my sin and in-to Thy-self, Je-sus, I come to Thee.
Out of dis-tress to ju-bi-lant psalm, Je-sus, I come to Thee.
Up-ward for aye on wings like a dove, Je-sus, I come to Thee
Ev-er Thy glo-rious face to be-hold, Je-sus, I come to Thee.

We Have an Anchor.

PRISCILLA J. OWENS.   WM. J. KIRKPATRICK.

1. Will your an-chor hold in the storms of life, When the clouds un-fold
2. It is safe-ly moored,'twill the storm with-stand, For 'tis well se-cured
3. It will firm-ly hold in the straits of fear, When the break-ers have
4. It will sure-ly hold in the floods of death, When the wa-ters cold
5. When our eyes be-hold thro' the gath-'ring night The city of gold,

their wings of strife? When the strong tides lift, and the ca-bles strain,
by the Sav-iour's hand; And the ca-bles, passed from His heart to mine,
told the reef is near, Tho' the tem-pest rave and the wild winds blow,
chill our lat-est breath, On the ris-ing tide it can nev-er fail,
our har-bor bright, We shall an-chor fast by the heav'n-ly shore,

CHORUS.

Will your an-chor drift, or firm re-main?
Can de-fy the blast,thro' strength di-vine.
Not an angry wave shall our bark o'er-flow.
While our hopes a-bide with-in the veil.
With the storms all past for-ev-er-more.

We have an an-chor that

keeps the soul stead-fast and sure while the bil-lows roll, Fast-ened to the

Rock which can-not move, Grounded firm and deep In the Sav-iour's love.

No. 26. The Shepherd Calls.

ELMER E. PERSON.

JAS. M. BLACK.

1. The shepherd stands at the open door,—He stands and waits for thee;
2. He's wait-ing at the out-er gate,—The gate of the o - pen fold;
3. Yield Him your hand, and heart and love,—O - bey the Shepherd's call.

He's calling now,—has called be - fore,—Oh, list - en to His plea.
Why lin - ger then or hes - i - tate? His love can - not be told.
Be numbered in that fold a - bove, Give Him your life, your all.

CHORUS.

He's call-ing, calling, calling you, Turn now, to-day, Make Him your choice.

He's call - ing, calling, calling you, Oh, list-en to the Shepherd's voice.

No. 27. There is Power in the Blood.

L. E. J

L. E. JONES.

1. Would you be free from your bur - den of sin, There's pow'r in the blood,
2. Would you be free from your pas - sion and pride, There's pow'r in the blood,
3. Would you be whit - er, much whit - er than snow, There's pow'r in the blood,
4. Would you do serv - ice for Je - sus your King, There's pow'r in the blood,

pow'r in the blood; Would you o'er e - vil a vic - to - ry win,
pow'r in the blood; Come for a cleans - ing to Cal - va - ry's tide,
pow'r in the blood; Sin stains are lost in its life - giv - ing flow,
pow'r in the blood; Would you live dai - ly, His prais - es to sing,

CHORUS.

There's won - der - ful pow'r in the blood. There is pow'r, pow'r,
there is pow'r,

Won - der work-ing pow'r in the blood of the Lamb, There is
in the blood, of the Lamb,

pow'r, pow'r, Wonder working pow'r, In the pre-cious blood of the Lamb.
there is pow'r,

Peace Through the Blood.

E. E. HEWITT.   A. J. SHOWALTER.

1. Come while God is call-ing, hear His word to-day, Peace thro' the
2. Sink the past for-ev-er 'neath the cleans-ing tide, Peace thro' the
3. Bless-ing free and boundless flow-ing from a-bove, Peace thro' the
4. Tell the joy-ful sto-ry ev-'ry-where you go, Peace thro' the

blood of the cross; Take the gift He of-fers, come without de-lay,
blood of the cross; Let the Ho-ly Spir-it in your heart a-bide,
blood of the cross; Ev-er-last-ing mer-cy, ev-er-last-ing love,
blood of the cross; Till the wide world o-ver, ransomed souls shall know,

CHORUS.

Peace thro' the blood of the cross.   Peace, ... won-der-ful
                                         Peace, wonder-ful peace!

peace! . . . .   Peace, ... wonder-ful peace! . . . .
peace, wonder-ful peace!   Peace, won-der-ful peace!   peace, won-der-ful peace!

1
Peace thro' the blood of the cross;

2
Peace thro' the blood of the cross.

I Cannot Let Him Go.

Mrs. S. A. Collins.

W. H. Doane.

1. One is stand-ing at the door, Hear Him knock, knock, knock, O my
2. Still He stand-eth at the door, Hear Him call, call, call, He has
3. Yes, He stand-eth at the door, See Him wait, wait, wait, Will He

heart wilt thou yield or no; Shall I now as oft ne-fore,
died for my guilt and sin; I am wea-ry and would rest,
leave and re-turn no more? No, that gen-tle voice so dear,

From my Sav-ior close the door, No, I can-not let Him go.
I may find it on His breast, I will quick-ly let Him in.
How it calms my ev-'ry fear, I will o-pen now the door.

CHORUS.

He stands and knocks, No, I can-not let Him go, Shall I
He stands and knocks, let Him go,

now as oft be-fore, From my Sav-ior close the door? No, I can-not let Him go!

Tell the Sweet Story.

Rev. Alfred J. Hough.   Jas. M. Black.

Moderato.

1. Tell the sto - ry, ten-der, sweet, At the Sav-ior's wounded feet I have
2. Tell the sto - ry o'er and o'er, I have o-pened wide the door Where the
3. Tell the sto - ry, ten-der, sweet, All its matchless strains re - peat,—Of a

found re-deem-ing mer - cy, full and free, And a flood of rapt-ure glows
Savior knocked and wait-ed day by day, Now His praise I love to sing,
soul redeemed and filled with love di - vine; Now for Christ a - lone I live,

In my heart and o - ver-flows, For the love of Je - sus saves e - ven me.
My Re-deem - er, Sav-ior, King, And His word my soul de-lights to o-bey.
And to Him my serv-ice give, For the love of Je - sus now is mine.

CHORUS.

Crown Him with glo - ry, Tell the sweet sto - ry, Tell the
Crown Him with glo - ry.   Tell the sweet sto - ry.

name, the fame of Je - sus far and wide, Crown Him with glo - ry,
far and wide.   Crown Him with glo - ry

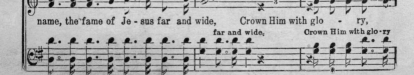

Tell the Sweet Story.

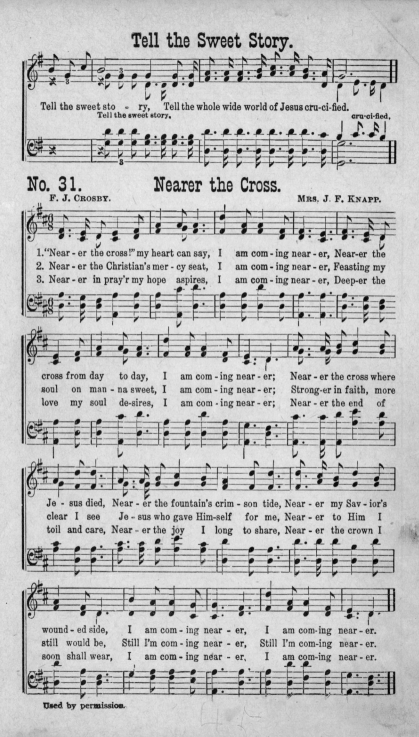

Tell the sweet sto - ry, Tell the whole wide world of Jesus cru-ci-fied.

Tell the sweet story.   cru-ci-fied,

No. 31. Nearer the Cross.

F. J. CROSBY.   MRS. J. F. KNAPP.

1. "Near - er the cross!" my heart can say, I am com - ing near - er, Near - er the
2. Near - er the Christian's mer - cy seat, I am com - ing near - er, Feasting my
3. Near - er in pray'r my hope aspires, I am com - ing near - er, Deep - er the

cross from day to day, I am com - ing near - er; Near - er the cross where
soul on man - na sweet, I am com - ing near - er; Strong-er in faith, more
love my soul de-sires, I am com - ing near - er; Near - er the end of

Je - sus died, Near - er the fountain's crim - son tide, Near - er my Sav - ior's
clear I see Je - sus who gave Him-self for me, Near - er to Him I
toil and care, Near - er the joy I long to share, Near - er the crown I

wound - ed side, I am com - ing near - er, I am com - ing near - er.
still would be, Still I'm com - ing near - er, Still I'm com - ing near - er.
soon shall wear, I am com - ing near - er, I am com - ing near - er.

Used by permission.

No. 32. He's Always Good to Me.

Rev. W. C. Martin.   Chas. G. Maynard.

1. The Mas - ter walks with me; He guides my trust-ing soul,
2. He gives me per-fect peace When storms are on the deep,
3. My walk with Christ is sweet; My soul is full of song

A ho - ly ray lights up the way to yon - der shin-ing goal.
I have no fear with Je - sus near,—He lulls my fears to sleep.
The sky is bright, my heart is light The whole good way a - long.

I'll fol - low where He lead - eth me With con - stant loy - al - ty,
He shields me un - der-neath His wings From foes I can - not see,
The love of God a - bout me falls Like man - na rich and free,

For, e - ven should the way seem dark, He's al - ways good to me.
My Fa - ther loves His trust - ing child, He's al - ways good to me.
And, though I can - not mer - it it, He's al - ways good to me.

CHORUS.

He's al - ways good to me, He's al - ways good to me,

He's Always Good to Me.

By night and day a - long the way, He's al - ways good to me.

No. 33. Every Day and Hour.

FANNY J. CROSBY.

WILLIAM H. DOANE.

1. Sav-iour, more than life to me, I am clinging, clinging, close to Thee;
2. Thro' this changing world be-low, Lead me gen-tly, gen-tly as I go;
3. Let me love Thee more and more, Till this fleet-ing, fleet-ing life is o'er;

Let Thy pre-cious blood ap-plied, Keep me ev-er, ev-er near Thy side.
Trust-ing Thee, I can-not stray, I can nev-er, nev-er lose my way.
Till my soul is lost in love, In a brighter, brighter world a-bove.

CHORUS.

Ev-'ry day, ev-'ry hour, Let me feel Thy cleansing pow'r;
Ev-'ry day and hour, ev-'ry day and hour,

May Thy ten - der love to me Bind me clos-er, clos-er, Lord, to Thee.

No. 34.   When Love Shines In.

Mrs. Frank A. Breck.   Wm. J. Kirkpatrick.

1. Je-sus comes with pow'r to gladden, When love shines in;   Ev-'ry life that
2. How the world will glow with beauty, When love shines in;   And the heart re-
3. Darkest sorrows will grow brighter, When love shines in;   And the heaviest
4. We may have un-fad-ing splendor, When love shines in;   And a friendship

woe can sad-den When love shines in;   Love will teach us how to pray;
joice in du-ty, When love shines in;   Tri-als may be sanc-ti-fied,
bur-den, light-er, When love shines in;   'Tis the glo-ry that will throw
true and ten-der, When love shines in;   When earth-vict'ries shall be won,

Love will drive the gloom away, Turn our darkness in-to day, When love shines in.
And the soul in peace a-bide, Life will all be glor-i-fied, When love shines in.
Light to show us where to go; O the heart shall blessing know When love shines in.
And our life in heav'n begun, There will be no need of sun, For love shines in.

Chorus.

When love shines in . . . When love shines in,   How the heart is
When love shines in, ...

When love shines in, When love shines in, When love shines in.

When Love Shines In.

tuned to singing, When love shines in; . . . When love shines in, . . . When
love shines in, Joy and peace to others bringing, When love shines in.

When love shines in; . . . . When love shines in. . . .
When love shines in, When love shines in.
When love shines in,
When love shines in.

No. 35.   Even Me.

Mrs. Eliz. Codner.   Wm. B. Bradbury.

1. { Lord, I hear of show'rs of bless-ing Thou art scatt'ring full and free— }
   { Show'rs, the thirsty land re-fresh-ing; Let some droppings fall on me— }

E - ven me, E - ven me, Let Thy bless-ing fall on me.

2 Pass me not, O gracious Father!
  Sinful though my heart may be;
  Thou might'st leave me, but the rather
  Let Thy mercy fall on me—
  Even me, etc.

3 Pass me not, O tender Saviour!
  Let me love and cling to Thee;
  I am longing for Thy favor;
  Whilst Thou'rt calling, O call me—
  Even me, etc.

4 Pass me not, O mighty Spirit!
  Thou canst make the blind to see;
  Witnesser, of Jesus' merit,
  Speak the word of power to me—
  Even me, etc.

5 Love of God, so pure and changeless;
  Blood of Christ, so rich and free;
  Grace of God, so rich and boundless;
  Magnify them all in me—
  Even me, etc.

No. 36. Full and Free Salvation.

MRS. ANNIE S. HAWKS. JAS. M. BLACK.

1. There is One who watches o'er us,— He has watch'd the a - ges through,
2. He is call-ing,—long has wait - ed For the com-ing of an hour,
3. He will en - ter not, un - bid - den, To re-lease a soul from sin;

With a love that nev-er chang-es, Giving peace and par-don too.
When, to Him in spir-it yield-ing, You would trust His grace and pow'r.
At your heart's door He is knocking, Will you rise and let Him in?

peace and par - don too.
His grace and pow'r.
rise and let Him in?

CHORUS.

There is full . . . and free sal - va - - tion, You have heard . . it

There is full and free sal - va - tion, free sal - va - tion, You have heard it,

o'er and o'er; Are you will - - ing, are you

you have heard it o'er and o'er; Are you will - ing, are you

read - y to be saved . . . . . for - ev - er - more?

read - y are you read - y to be saved for - ev - er - more, for - ev - er - more?

No. 37.   His Way With Thee.

C. S. N.

Rev. Cyrus S. Nusbaum.

1. Would you live for Je-sus, and be al-ways pure and good? Would you walk with
2. Would you have Him make you free, and fol-low at His call? Would you know the
3. Would you in His king-dom find a place of constant rest? Would you prove Him

Him with-in the nar-row road? Would you have Him bear your bur-den,
peace that comes by giv-ing all? Would you have Him save you, so that
true each prov-i-den-tial test? Would you in His serv-ice la-bor

CHORUS:

car-ry all your load? Let Him have His way with thee.
you need nev-er fall? Let Him have His way with thee. His pow'r can make you
al-ways at your best? Let Him have His way with thee.

what you ought to be; His blood can cleanse your heart and make you free; His love can

rit.

fill your soul, and you will see 'Twas best for Him to have His way with thee.

No. 38. Winning Precious Souls to Thee.

E. A. H.
ELISHA A. HOFFMAN.

1. Be with us, Lord, as forth we go, Win-ning pre-cious souls to Thee;
2. Help us to la-bor faith-ful-ly, Win-ning pre-cious souls to Thee;
3. We toil with fee-ble hands and weak, Win-ning pre-cious souls to Thee;
4. As we each day our work pur-sue, Win-ning pre-cious souls to Thee;
5. We need Thy help, O gra-cious Lord! Win-ning pre-cious souls to Thee;
6. As we go forth in trust and love, Win-ning pre-cious souls to Thee;

And make our love and zeal to glow Win-ning pre-cious souls to Thee.
And gath-er ma-ny sheaves for Thee, Win-ning pre-cious souls to Thee.
To us new faith and cour-age speak, Win-ning pre-cious souls to Thee.
Our faith increase, our zeal re-new, Win-ning pre-cious souls to Thee.
Go with us, and Thy aid af-ford, Win-ning pre-cious souls to Thee.
Send down Thy bless-ing from a-bove, Win-ning pre-cious souls to Thee.

CHORUS.

Winning precious souls, ma-ny pre-cious souls, Jew-els in Thy crown to be;

Help us bring them in from the ways of sin, Many precious souls to Thee.

No. 39.   Oh! 'tis Glory in My Soul.

FLORA L. BEST.   JNO. R. SWENEY. By per.

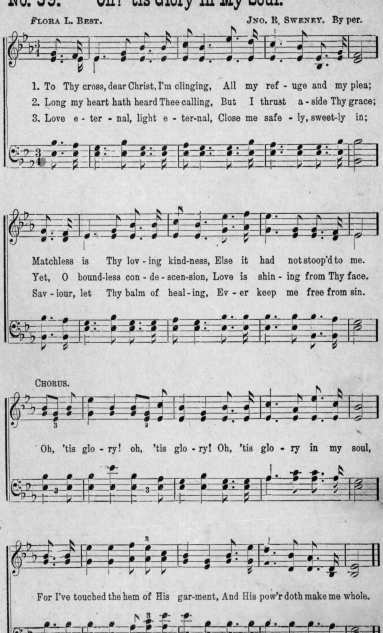

1. To Thy cross, dear Christ, I'm clinging, All my ref - uge and my plea;
2. Long my heart hath heard Thee calling, But I thrust a - side Thy grace;
3. Love e - ter - nal, light e - ter-nal, Close me safe - ly, sweet-ly in;

Matchless is Thy lov - ing kind-ness, Else it had not stoop'd to me.
Yet, O bound-less con - de - scen-sion, Love is shin - ing from Thy face.
Sav - iour, let Thy balm of heal-ing, Ev - er keep me free from sin.

CHORUS.

Oh, 'tis glo - ry! oh, 'tis glo - ry! Oh, 'tis glo - ry in my soul,

For I've touched the hem of His gar-ment, And His pow'r doth make me whole.

No. 40. Wonderful Peace.

Rev. W. D. Cornell. Alt. Rev. W. G. Cooper.

1. Far a-way in the depths of my spir-it to-night, Rolls a
2. What a treas-ure I have in this won-der-ful peace, Bur-ied
3. I am rest-ing to-night in this won-der-ful peace, Rest-ing
4. And me thinks when I rise to that cit-y of peace, Where the
5. Ah! soul, are you here with-out com-fort or rest, Marching

mel-o-dy sweet-er than psalm; In ce-les-tial like strains it un-
deep in the heart of my soul; So se-cure that no pow-er can
sweet-ly in Je-sus' con-trol; For I'm kept from all dan-ger by
Au-thor of peace I shall see, That one strain of the song which is
down the rough path-way of time! Make Je-sus your friend ere the

ceas-ing-ly falls O'er my soul like an in-fi-nite calm.
mine it a-way, While the years of e-ter-ni-ty roll.
night and by day, And His glo-ry is flood-ing my soul.
ran-somed will sing, In that heav-en-ly king-dom will be.
shad-ows grow dark; Oh, ac-cept of this peace so sub-lime.

CHORUS.

Peace! Peace! Wonder-ful peace, Coming down from the Fa-ther a-bove; Sweep

o-ver my spir-it for-ev-er, I pray, In fath-om-less billows of love.

No. 41.   I Must Tell Jesus.

E, A. H.

Rev. E. A. HOFFMAN.

1. I must tell Je - sus all of my tri - als; I can - not bear these
2. I must tell Je - sus all of my troub - les, He is a kind, com-
3. Tempted and tried I need a great Sav - iour, One who can help my
4. O how the world to e - vil al - lures me? O how my heart is

bur - dens a - lone; In my dis - tress He kind - ly will help me;
pas - sion - ate Friend; If I but ask Him, He will de - liv - er,
bur - dens to bear; I must tell Je - sus, I must tell Je - sus;
tempt - ed to sin! I must tell Je - sus, and He will help me

CHORUS.

He ev - er loves and cares for His own.
Make of my troub - les quick - ly an end.   I must tell Je - sus! I must tell
He all my cares and sor - rows will share.
O - ver the world the vic - t'ry to win.

Je - sus! I can - not bear my bur - dens a - lone; I must tell

rit.

Je - sus! I must tell Je - sus! Je - sus can help me, Je - sus a - lone.

No. 42.   It Was Spoken for the Master.

Lizzie Edwards.   Wm. J. Kirkpatrick.

1. It was spo-ken for the Mas-ter, Oh, how lov-ing-ly it fell!
2. Oh, we know not when we scat-ter, Where the pre-cious seed will fall,
3. When our bus-y toil is o-ver, From the vine-yard when we go,

It was ut-tered in a whis-per, Who had breathed it none could tell.
But we work and trust in Je-sus, For He watcheth o-ver all.
We shall find a store of bless-ings That on earth we could not know.

It was spo-ken for the Mas-ter, On-ly just a lit-tle word,
We may sow be-side the wa-ters Of af-flic-tion, it may be,
We shall won-der at the brightness Of the crowns we then shall wear,

But the chords that long had slumbered, In a grief-worn heart were stirred.
But the fruits of ear-nest la-bor At the reap-ing we shall see.
But the Lord Him-self will tell us Why He placed the jew-els there.

REFRAIN.

Gen-tle words of pa-tient kindness, Tho' un-heed-ed oft they seem,

It was Spoken for the Master.

ad lib.

To the fold of grace may gath-er Souls of which we lit-tle dream.

No. 43. It is Well with My Soul.

H. G. SPAFFORD.

P. P. BLISS.

1. When peace, like a riv - er, at - tend-eth my way, When sor-rows, like
2. Tho' Sa - tan should buf - fet, tho' tri - als should come, Let this blest as -
3. My sin,— oh, the bliss of this glo - ri - ous tho't—My sin—not in
4. And, Lord, haste the day when the faith shall be sight, The clouds be rolled

sea - bil - lows, roll; What-ev - er my lot, Thou hast taught me to
sur - ance con - trol, That Christ hath re - gard - ed my help - less es -
part but the whole, Is nailed to His cross and I bear it no
back as a scroll, The trump shall re - sound, and the Lord shall de -

CHORUS.

say, It is well, it is well with my soul. It is well . . .
tate, And hath shed His own blood for my soul.
more, Praise the Lord, praise the Lord, O my soul!
scend, "E - ven so"— it is well with my soul. It is

. . . with my soul, ... It is well, it is well with my soul.
well with my soul,

No. 44. The Grand Old Story of Salvation.

E. E. HEWITT. WM. J. KIRKPATRICK.

1. We tell it as we jour-ney toward the man-sions built a - bove, The
2. His hand can lift the fall - en and His blood can make them white, The
3. We'll sing it in the bat - tle, and its notes shall vic - t'ry be, The
4. The an - gels look with won-der, yet their harps can nev - er tell, The

grand old sto - ry of sal - va-tion; We sing it out with gladness, in the
grand old sto - ry of sal - va-tion; His love can pierce the darkness with a
grand old sto - ry of sal - va-tion; We'll sing it in our tri - als, till the
grand old sto - ry of sal - va-tion; His ransom'd, clothed with beauty, shall the

mel - o - dies of love, The grand old sto - ry of sal - va - tion.
nev - er - fad - ing light, The grand old sto - ry of sal - va - tion.
pass - ing shad - ows flee, The grand old sto - ry of sal - va - tion.
praise of Je - sus swell, The grand old sto - ry of sal - va - tion.

CHORUS.

Ring it out, ring it out, Ring to
Ring it out. ring it out,

ev - 'ry tribe and na - tion, Ring it out ev - 'ry-where,

The Grand Old Story.

Ring it out ev - 'ry-where, The grand old sto - ry of sal - va - tion.

No. 45.   Is Thy Heart Right with God?

E. A. H.   ELISHA A. HOFFMAN.

1. Have thy af - fections been nailed to the cross? Is thy heart right with God?
2. Hast thou do - min - ion o'er self and o'er sin? Is thy heart right with God?
3. Is there no more condem - na - tion for sin? Is thy heart right with God?
4. Are all thy pow'rs un - der Je - sus' con - trol? Is thy heart right with God?
5. Art thou now walk-ing in heaven's pure light? Is thy heart right with God?

Dost thou count all things for Je - sus but loss? Is thy heart right with God?
O - ver all e - vil with - out and with - in? Is thy heart right with God?
Does Je - sus rule in the tem - ple with - in? Is thy heart right with God?
Does He each mo - ment a - bide in thy soul? Is thy heart right with God?
Is thy soul wearing the gar - ment of white? Is thy heart right with God?

CHORUS.

Is thy heart right with God, Wash'd in the crim - son flood, Cleans'd and made

ho - ly, hum - ble and low - ly, Right in the sight of God? of God?

No. 46.   Thou Canst Save.

Rev. W. J. H. Hogan.   Chas. H. Gabriel.

1. In life's long-est, fierc-est bat-tle, Thou wilt keep me, Sav-ior
2. When my faith, in tri-al, wav-ers, Hast-en, Lord, Thine aid af-
3. Come what may, then, calm or tem-pest, Light or dark-ness, joy or

mine;   When the tem-pest wild-ly rag-es, Keep me
ford;   Give me some sweet glimpse of glo-ry, Speak some
woe;   By Thy pres-ence cheer'd, de-fend-ed, I shall

CHORUS.

in Thy love di-vine. Thou canst save me, Thou canst
strength-in-spir-ing word.
fear no storm nor foe.
Thou canst save me,

hold me, Dear-est Sav-ior, Thou a-lone, May I
Thou canst hold me, Dear-est Sav-ior,

stand se-cure-ly, ev-er, On the sure foun-da-tion stone.

Copyright, 1900, by Jas. M. Black,

No. 47. Speed for Thy Life.

FANNY J. CROSBY.   W. H. DOANE.

1. Speed, for thy life to the mount-ain, Slight not the mes-sage di-vine,
2. Speed for thy life to the mount-ain, List to the warn-ing a-gain;
3. Speed, for the day is de-clin-ing, Soon its bright moments will fade;
4. Speed for thy life to the mount-ain, Fly like a bird to its nest,

Dan-ger and death are be-fore thee, Haste, while the hours are thine.
For-ward, and look not be-hind thee, Stay not in all the plain.
What if a storm should o'er-take thee, Where would thou turn for aid?
Fly to the arms of the Sav-ior: There is thy on-ly rest.

CHORUS.

Speed thee, speed thee, Shad-ows a-round thee are fall-ing;
Speed thee a-way, hear and o-bey,

Speed thee, speed thee, Come while the Sav-ior is call-ing.
Speed thee a-way, hear and o-bey,

No. 48. Patiently Pleading.

JAMES ROWE. Duet. WM. J. KIREPATRICK.

1. Je - sus is plead - ing, Pa-tient-ly plead - ing, Sweet-ly and ten - der - ly,
2. Moments are speed-ing, Still He is plead - ing; Much He has suf - fered thy
3. Je - sus is plead-ing, Ten - der - ly plead - ing: Sin - ner, no long - er re-

sin - ner with thee; He will re-ceive thee, Comfort, relieve thee, Seek Him this
soul to re - deem; Sore - ly to need Him, Sure-ly to heed Him, Hasten at
sist that sweet voice; Gladly He'll meet thee, Lovingly greet thee; Trust Him com-

CHORUS.

mo - ment, sal - va - tion is free.
once to the soul-cleans-ing stream. Go not a - way, Seek Him to - day,
plete - ly, be saved and re - joice.

For He is wait - ing thy Sav - ior to be; Nev - er-more grieve Him

Come and re - ceive Him; Free - ly He of - fers a par - don for thee,

At the Cross.

R. E. Hudson. By per.

1. A - las! and did my Sav - ior bleed, And did my Sov-'reign die,
2. Was it for crimes that I have done, He groaned up - on the tree?
3. But drops of grief can ne'er re-pay, The debt of love I owe;

Would He de-vote that sa - cred head For such a worm as I?
A - maz - ing pit - y, grace unknown, And love be-yond de - gree!
Here, Lord, I give my - self a-way, 'Tis all that I can do!

CHORUS.

At the cross, at the cross, where I first saw the light, And the

bur-den of my heart rolled a - way— rolled a - way, It was there by faith

I re-ceived my sight, And now I am hap-py all the day.

No. 50. Blessings.

CHARLOTTE G. HOMER.

CHAS. H. GABRIEL.

1. There are blessings gen-tly fall-ing on us like the rain In such dai-ly
2. When a-mid the con-flict, and the light of faith is dim, Would that we might
3. Have we an-y mer-it of our own by which to claim Life, or death, or
4. Let us look a-bout us—let us search our hearts and see What our lives, with-

show-ers, that to count them is in vain; Blessings numbered on-ly by the
en-ter dark Geth-sem-a-ne with Him; Then we might dis-cov-er how a
com-fort or to e-ven call His name? Yet, in sel-fish moments, doubts and
out His pa-tient, watchful care would be; Did He for a moment fail to

sands up-on the shore, 'Till, indeed, we wonder that there's room for an-y more.
ten-der, lov-ing hand Gen-tly leads us onward, upward to a bet-ter land.
fear be-fore us rise 'Till His love and goodness all are hid-den from our eyes.
keep us in His care, We should vanish quickly as the light'ning in the air.

CHORUS.

Bless - ings! O what glo - ry, Bless - ings!
Bless-ings! O what glo-ry, O what matchless glo-ry, Bless-ings! tell the sto-

tell the sto - - ry, It will give you help and strength to
ry, tell the won-drous sto-ry;

Blessings.

la - bor on, As sun-light gives the morn-ing when the night is gone.

No. 51. Ready to Do His Will.

S. E. L.

CHARLIE D. TILLMAN.

1. Read-y to suf-fer grief or pain, Read-y to stand the test;
2. Read-y to go, read-y to bear, Read-y to watch and pray;
3. Read-y to speak, read-y to think, Read-y with heart and brain;
4. Read-y to speak, read-y to warn, Read-y o'er souls to yearn;

Read-y to stay at home and send Oth-ers if He sees best.
Read-y to stand a - side and give, Till He shall clear the way,
Read-y to stand where He sees fit, Read-y to stand the strain.
Read-y in life, read-y in death, Read-y for His re - turn.

CHORUS.

Read-y to go, read-y to stay, Read-y my place to fill;

Read-y for serv - ice, low-ly or great, Read-y to do His will.

No. 52. I'll Go Where You Want Me to Go.

MARY BROWN.

CARRIE F. ROUNSEFELL.

Andante.

1. It may not be on the mountain's height, Or o - ver the storm-y sea;
2. Per-haps to-day there are lov-ing words Which Je - sus would have me speak—
3. There's surely somewhere a low - ly place, In earth's harvest fields so wide—

It may not be at the bat-tle's front My Lord will have need of me;
There may be now in the paths of sin Some wand'rer whom I should seek—
Where I may la - bor thro' life's short day For Je - sus the cru - ci - fied—

But, if by a still, small voice He calls To paths that I do not know,
O Sav - ior, if Thou wilt be my guide, Tho' dark and rugged the way,
So trust-ing my all to Thy ten - der care, And know-ing Thou lov - est me,

I'll an-swer, dear Lord, with my hand in Thine, I'll go where you want me to go
My voice shall ech - o Thy mes-sage sweet, I'll say what you want me to say.
I'll do Thy will with a heart sin-cere, I'll be what you want me to be.

REFRAIN.

I'll go where you want me to go, dear Lord, O - ver mountain, or plain, or sea;

I'll Go Where You Want Me to Go.

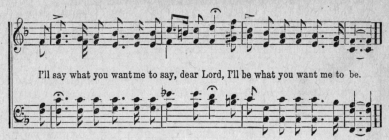

I'll say what you want me to say, dear Lord, I'll be what you want me to be.

No. 53.   More Love to Thee, O Christ.

Mrs. E. Prentiss.   Dr. W. H. Doane.

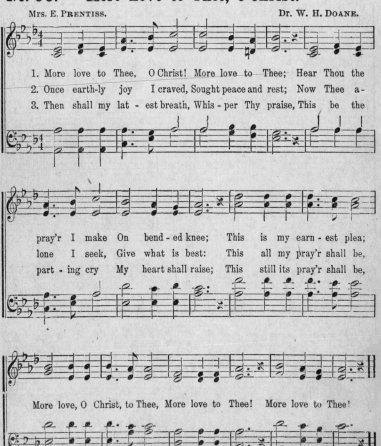

1. More love to Thee, O Christ! More love to Thee; Hear Thou the
2. Once earth-ly joy I craved, Sought peace and rest; Now Thee a-
3. Then shall my lat - est breath, Whis - per Thy praise, This be the

pray'r I make On bend - ed knee; This is my earn - est plea;
lone I seek, Give what is best: This all my pray'r shall be,
part - ing cry My heart shall raise; This still its pray'r shall be,

More love, O Christ, to Thee, More love to Thee! More love to Thee!

No. 54. When I Stand On the Streets of Gold.

A. N. O.

JAS. M. BLACK.

Slow, with expression.

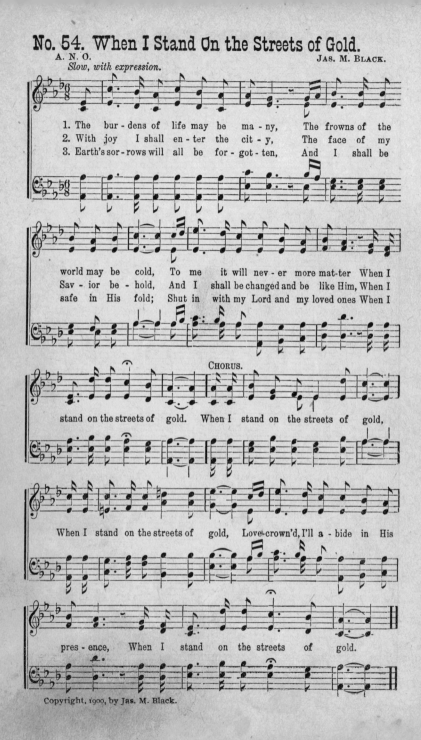

1. The bur - dens of life may be ma - ny, The frowns of the
2. With joy I shall en - ter the cit - y, The face of my
3. Earth's sor - rows will all be for - got - ten, And I shall be

world may be cold, To me it will nev - er more mat - ter When I
Sav - ior be - hold, And I shall be changed and be like Him, When I
safe in His fold; Shut in with my Lord and my loved ones When I

CHORUS.

stand on the streets of gold. When I stand on the streets of gold,

When I stand on the streets of gold, Love-crown'd, I'll a - bide in His

pres - ence, When I stand on the streets of gold.

No. 55. Draw Me Nearer.

FANNY J. CROSBY. W. H. DOANE.

1. I am thine; O Lord, I have heard thy voice, And it told thy
2. Con-se-crate me now to thy serv-ice, Lord, By the pow'r of
3. O the pure de-light of a sin-gle hour That be-fore thy
4. There are depths of love that I can-not know Till I cross the

love to me; But I long to rise in the arms of faith,
grace di-vine; Let my soul look up with a stead-fast hope,
throne I spend, When I kneel in pray'r, and with thee, my God,
nar-row sea, There are heights of joy that I may not reach,

CHORUS.

And be clos-er drawn to thee. Draw me near-er,
And my will be lost in thine.
I com-mune as friend with friend.
Till I rest in peace with thee. near-er, near-er,

near-er, bless-ed Lord To the cross where thou hast died; Draw me

near-er, near-er, near-er, blessed Lord, To thy precious, bleed-ing side.

No. 56. Jesus is All the World to Me.

W. L. T.

WILL L. THOMPSON.

1. Je - sus is all the world to me, My life, my joy, my all;
2. Je - sus is all the world to me, My friend in tri - als sore;
3. Je - sus is all the world to me, And true to Him I'll be;
4. Je - sus is all the world to me, I want no bet - ter friend;

He is my strength from day to day, With - out Him I would fall.
I go to Him for bless-ings and He gives them o'er and o'er.
O, how could I this friend de - ny, When He's so true to me?
I trust Him now, I'll trust Him when Life's fleet - ing days shall end.

When I am sad, to Him I go, No oth - er one can cheer me so;
He sends the sun-shine and the rain, He sends the har-vest's gold - en grain;
Fol - low-ing Him I know I'm right, He watch-es o'er me day and night;
Beau - ti - ful life with such a friend; Beau - ti - ful life that has no end;

When I am sad He makes me glad, He's my friend.
Sun - shine and rain, har - vest of grain, He's my friend.
Fol - low-ing Him, by day and night, He's my friend.
E - ter - nal life, e - ter - nal joy, He's my friend.

No. 57. Jesus Saves.

Priscilla J. Owens. Wm. J. Kirkpatrick.

1. We have heard a joy - ful sound, Je - sus saves, Je - sus saves;
2. Waft it on the roll - ing tide, Je - sus saves, Je - sus saves;
3. Sing a - bove the bat - tle's strife, Je - sus saves, Je - sus saves;
4. Give the winds a might - y voice, Je - sus saves, Je - sus saves;

Spread the glad - ness all a - round, Je - sus saves, Je - sus saves;
Tell to sin - ners, far and wide, Je - sus saves, Je - sus saves;
By his death and end - less life, Je - sus saves, Je - sus saves;
Let the na - tions now re - joice, Je - sus saves, Je - sus saves;

Bear the news to ev - 'ry land, Climb the steeps and cross the waves,
Sing, ye is - lands of the sea, Ech - o back, ye o - cean caves,
Sing it soft - ly thro' the gloom, When the heart for mer - cy craves.
Shout sal - va - tion full and free, High - est hill and deep - est caves,

On - ward, 'tis our Lord's com - mand, Je - sus saves, Je - sus saves.
Earth shall keep her Ju - bi - lee, Je - sus saves, Je - sus saves.
Sing in tri - umph o'er the tomb, Je - sus saves, Je - sus saves.
This our song of vic - to - ry, Je - sus saves, Je - sus saves.

No. 58. Leaning On the Everlasting Arms.

Rev. E. A. Hoffman.   A. J. Showalter.

1. What a fel - low-ship, what a joy di - vine, Lean - ing on the ev - er-
2. Oh, how sweet to walk in this pil-grim way, Lean - ing on the ev - er-
3. What have I to dread, what hnve I to fear, Lean - ing on the ev - er-

last - ing Arms! What a bless - ed - ness, what a peace is mine,
last - ing Arms! Oh, how bright the path grows from day to day,
last - ing Arms? I have bless - ed peace with my Lord so near,

CHORUS.

Lean - ing on the ev - er - last - ing Arms! Lean - - ing,
Lean - ing on Je - sus,

lean - - ing, Safe and se-cure from all a - larms, Lean - ing,
lean - ing on Je - sus,   Lean - ing on Je - sus,

lean - - ing, Lean - ing on the ev - er - last - ing Arms.
lean - ing on Je - sus,

No. 59. The Savior Precious.

JAMES S. APPLE.   JNO. R. SWENEY.

1. { I have found the Sav - ior pre-cious, And I love Him more and more;
   { I have found the Sav - ior pre-cious, And I find Him pre-cious still;
2. { I have found the Sav - ior pre-cious, And, wher-ev - er I may go,
   { I am read - y, if He calls me, In the bat-tle front to stand;
3. { I have found the Sav - ior pre-cious; Hal - le - lu - jah! praise His name!
   { I have found the Sav - ior pre-cious; He has prov'd my dear-est Friend;

He has rolled a - way my bur - den, And my mourning days are o'er; }
All my life is con - se - crat-ed To His (*Omit.*) . . . . . }
I will bear the roy - al stand-ard, And its col - ors I vill show; }
I am read - y—yes, and wait-ing—To ful (*Omit.*) . . . . . }
To a man-sion in His kingdom Thro' His grace the right I claim. }
And my faith can trust His prom-ise Of pro- (*Omit.*) . . . . . }

CHORUS.

serv-ice and His will. I have tak - en up the cross, And will
fill my Lord's command.
tec-tion to the end. I have tak - en up the cross, And will nev - er lay it down, I have

nev - er lay it down Till I see . . . . His face in
tak-en up the cross And will nev-er lay it down Till I see His face in glo - ry, Till I

glo - - ry, And re - ceive . . . . a star-ry crown.
see His face in glo - ry, And re - ceive a star-ry crown, a star-ry crown.

The Stranger at the Door.

T. C. O.

T. C. O'KANE.

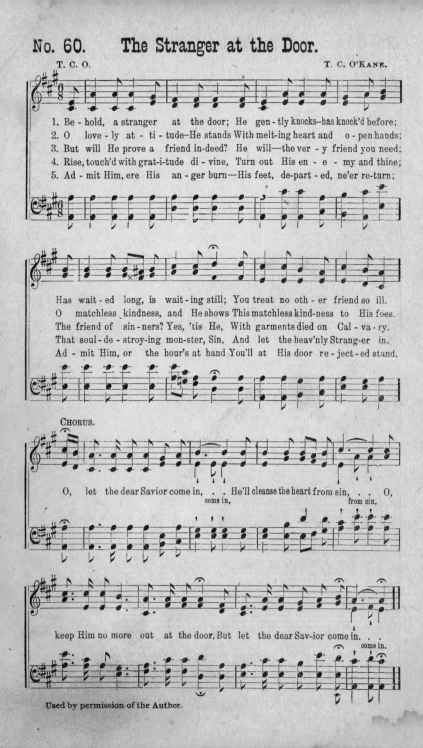

1. Be - hold, a stranger at the door; He gen - tly knocks—has knock'd before;
2. O love - ly at - ti - tude—He stands With melt-ing heart and o - pen hands;
3. But will He prove a friend in-deed? He will—the ver - y friend you need;
4. Rise, touch'd with grat-i-tude di - vine, Turn out His en - e - my and thine;
5. Ad - mit Him, ere His an - ger burn—His feet, de-part - ed, ne'er re-turn;

Has wait - ed long, is wait-ing still; You treat no oth - er friend so ill.
O matchless kindness, and He shows This matchless kind-ness to His foes.
The friend of sin - ners? Yes, 'tis He, With garments died on Cal - va - ry.
That soul - de - stroy-ing mon-ster, Sin, And let the heav'nly Strang-er in.
Ad - mit Him, or the hour's at hand You'll at His door re - ject - ed stand.

CHORUS.

O, let the dear Savior come in, .. He'll cleanse the heart from sin, .. O,
come in, from sin,

keep Him no more out at the door, But let the dear Sav-ior come in. ..
come in.

Used by permission of the Author.

No. 61.   Sunshine in the Soul.

E. E. HEWITT.

JNO. R. SWENEY.

1. There's sun-shine in my soul to-day, More glo - ri - ous and bright
2. There's mu - sic in my soul to-day, A car - ol to my King;
3. There's springtime in my soul to - day, For when the Lord is near,
4. There's glad-ness in my soul to - day, And hope, and praise, and love,

Than glows in an - y earth-ly sky, For Je - sus is my light.
And Je - sus, lis - ten-ing, can hear The songs I can - not sing.
The dove of peace sings in my heart, The flow'rs of grace ap - pear.
For bless-ings which He gives me now, For joys "laid up" a - bove.

REFRAIN.

Oh, there's sun - - - - - shine, bless - ed sun - - - - shine,
Oh, there's sun - shine in the soul, bless - ed sun-shine in the soul.

While the peace - ful, hap - py mo - ments roll;   When
hap - py mo-ments roll;

Je - sus shows His smil - ing face, There is sun-shine in my soul.

No. 62. Wonderful Story of Love.

J. M. D.

Rev. J. M. Driver, by per.

1. Won-der-ful sto-ry of love: Tell it to me a-gain;
2. Won-der-ful sto-ry of love: Tho' you are far a-way;
3. Won-der-ful sto-ry of love: Je-sus pro-vides a rest:

Won-der-ful sto-ry of love: Wake the im-mor-tal strain!
Won-der-ful sto-ry of love: Still He doth call to-day;
Won-der-ful sto-ry of love: For all the pure and blest,

An-gels with rapt-ure an-nounce it, Shepherds with won-der re-ceive it;
Call-ing from Cal-va-ry's mountain, Down from the crys-tal bright fountain,
Rest in those man-sions a-bove us, With those who've gone on be-fore us,

Sin-ner, oh! won't you be-lieve it? Won-der-ful sto-ry of love.
E'en from the dawn of cre-a-tion, Won-der-ful sto-ry of love.
Sing-ing the rapt-ur-ous cho-rus, Won-der-ful sto-ry of love.

FINE.

D. S.—Won-der-ful sto-ry of love!

CHORUS.

D. S.

Won - der - ful! won - der - ful! Won - der - ful!
Won-der-ful sto-ry of love: won-der-ful sto-ry of love: Won-der-ful sto-ry of love:

No. 63.   Love Divine.

CHARLES WESLEY.   JOHN ZUNDEL.

1. Love di-vine, all love ex-cel-ling, Joy of heav'n, to earth come down!
2. Breathe, O breathe Thy lov-ing Spir-it In-to ev-'ry troub-led breast!
3. Come, Al-might-y to de-liv-er, Let us all Thy life re-ceive;
4. Fin-ish, then, Thy new cre-a-tion; Pure and spot-less let us be;

Fix in us Thy hum-ble dwell-ing; All Thy faith-ful mer-cies crown.
Let us all in Thee in-her-it, Let us find that sec-ond rest.
Sud-den-ly re-turn, and nev-er, Nev-er-more Thy tem-ples leave;
Let us see Thy great sal-va-tion, Per-fect-ly re-stored in Thee.

Je-sus, Thou art all com-pas-sion, Pure, un-bound-ed love Thou art;
Take a-way our bent to sin-ning, Al-pha and O-me-ga be;
Thee we would be al-ways blessing, Serve Thee as Thy hosts a-bove,
Chang'd from glo-ry in-to glo-ry, Till in heav'n we take our place,

Vis-it us with Thy sal-va-tion; En-ter ev-'ry trem-bling heart.
End of faith, as its be-gin-ning, Set our hearts at lib-er-ty.
Pray and praise Thee with-out ceas-ing, Glo-ry in Thy per-fect love.
Till we cast our crowns be-fore Thee, Lost in won-der, love, and praise.

No. 64.   Lead and Keep Me.

HARRIET E. JONES.   H. A. HENRY.

1. Lov-ing Saviour, lead Thou me, . . . Lest I wander far from Thee, . . .
2. Oh, Thou ref-uge of my soul, . . . Hold me in di-vine con-trol; . . .
3. Sav-iour, keep me day by day, . . . All a-long my pil-grim way; . . .

1. Lov - ing Saviour, lead Thou me, Lest I wander far from Thee.

I am safe when in Thy care, . . Thou wilt keep from ev-'ry snare.
What-so-ev-er may be-tide, . . . Lead and keep me by Thy side.
When my earthly work is done, . . . Lead me home, O bless-ed One.

I am safe when in Thy care,

CHORUS.

Lead me, lead me, Saviour, lead me all the way, . .

Lead me, O my Sav-iour, nev-er let me stray, lead me,

This my constant pray'r shall be, . . . Sav-iour, lead me home to Thee.

This my constant pray'r shall be,

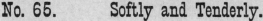

No. 65. Softly and Tenderly.

W. L. T.   WILL L. THOMPSON.

Very slow.

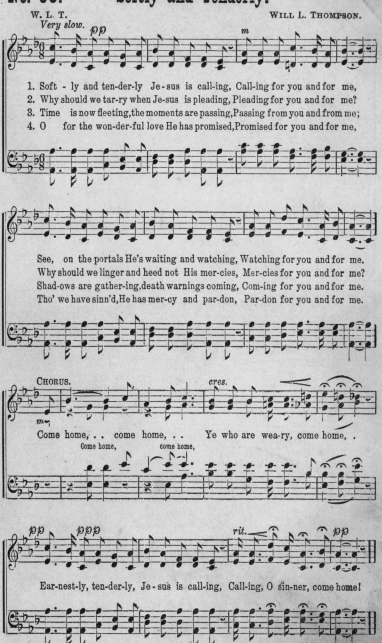

1. Soft - ly and ten-der-ly Je-sus is call-ing, Call-ing for you and for me,
2. Why should we tar-ry when Je-sus is pleading, Pleading for you and for me?
3. Time   is now fleeting, the moments are passing, Passing from you and from me;
4. O   for the won-der-ful love He has promised, Promised for you and for me,

See,   on the portals He's waiting and watching, Watching for you and for me.
Why should we linger and heed not His mer-cies, Mer-cies for you and for me?
Shad-ows are gather-ing, death warnings coming, Com-ing for you and for me.
Tho' we have sinn'd, He has mer-cy and par-don, Par-don for you and for me.

CHORUS.   *cres.*

Come home, . . come home, . .   Ye who are wea-ry, come home, .
Come home,   come home,

Ear-nest-ly, ten-der-ly, Je-sus is call-ing, Call-ing, O sin-ner, come home!

No. 66. Walk Beside Me.

KATHARINE E. PURVIS. JAS. M. BLACK.

1. Walk be-side me, O my Savior, While life's morning sky is bright; Grant me
2. When the noontide's glowing splendor Brings its weight of toil and care, May thy
3. When the twilight shades, descending, Warn my soul that night is near, With the

now thy loving favor, Flood my path with heav'nly light Whether good or
love, so pure and tender, All my heav-y burdens bear! In a wea-ry
hues of sunset blending, Let the light of heaven appear, Through the valley,

ill betide me, Whether skies be dark or clear, Ev-er stay so close be-
land, provide me Sheltering rock and cooling spring; When the temp-est rages,
Savior, take me, Close my eyes when night shall come, Then bid an-gel voic-es

CHORUS.

side me I may know and feel thee near.
hide me Underneath thy fold-ed wing. Blessed Savior, walk with me, Take a
wake me, Sweetly singing, "Welcome home."

way all anxious fear; Ever stay so close beside me, I may know and feel thee near.

No. 67.   Saved by Grace.

(Solo or Duet.)

FANNY J. CROSBY.   GEO. C. STEBBINS.

1. Some day the sil - ver cord will break, And I no more as now shall sing;
2. Some day my earth - ly house will fall, I can-not tell how soon 'twill be,
3. Some day, when fades the gold - en sun Beneath the ro - sy-tint - ed west,
4. Some day; till then I'll watch and wait, My lamp all trimm'd and burning bright,

But, O, the joy when I shall wake With-in the pal - ace of the King!
But this I know—my All in All Has now a place in heav'n for me.
My bless-ed Lord shall say, "Well done!" And I shall en - ter in - to rest.
That when my Sav - ior ope's the gate, My soul to Him may take its flight.

CHORUS.

And I shall see   Him face to face,   And tell the sto-ry—Saved by grace;
       shall see   to face,

rit.

And I shall see   Him face to face,   And tell the sto-ry—Saved by grace.
       shall see   to face,

No. 68.   Seeking the Lost.

W. A. O.

W. A. OGDEN.

1. Seek-ing the lost, yes, kind-ly en-treat-ing, Wan-der-ers on the
2. Seek-ing the lost, and point-ing to Je-sus, Souls that are weak, and
3. Thus I would go on mis-sions of mer-cy, Fol-low-ing Christ from

mount-ain a-stray: "Come un-to me," His mes-sage re-peat-ing,
hearts that are sore; Lead-ing them forth in ways of sal-va-tion,
day un-to day; Cheer-ing the faint, and rais-ing the fall-en;

CHORUS.

Words of the Mas-ter speaking to-day.
Show-ing the path to life ev-er-more.
Point-ing the lost to Je-sus the way.

Go-ing a-far

Go-ing a-far.........

up-on the mountain,   Bringing the wand'rer back a-

up-on the mount-ain,.... Bring-ing the wan - - d'rer back a-

Used by permission.

Seeking the Lost.

gain, back again, In-to the fold of my Redeem-er,

gain,...... In-to the fold...... of my Re-deem-er,....

Je-sus, the Lamb for sin - ners slain, for sin - ners slain.

Je - sus the Lamb........ for sin - ners slain..........

No. 69.   Nearer, My God, to Thee.

SARAH F. ADAMS.   LOWELL MASON.

1. Near - er, my God, to Thee, Near-er to Thee; E'en tho' it be a cross
2. Tho' like a wan-der-er, The sun gone down, Darkness be o - ver me,
3. There let the way ap-pear Steps un - to heav'n; All that Thou send-est me,
4. Then, with my waking tho'ts Bright with Thy praise, Out of my ston-y griefs,
5. Or if, on joy - ful wing, Cleaving the sky, Sun, moon, and stars for-got,

D. S.—Near - er, my God, to Thee,

FINE.   D. S.

That rais-eth me; Still all my song shall be, Near - er, my God, to Thee,
My rest a stone; Yet in my dreams I'd be, Near - er, my God, to Thee,
In mer - cy giv'n; An - gels to beck-on me Near - er, my God, to Thee,
Beth - el I'll raise; So by my woes to be Near - er, my God, to Thee,
Up - ward I fly; Still all my song shall be, Near - er, my God, to Thee,

Near - er to Thee!

No. 70. My Redeemer.

P. P. BLISS.   JAS. MCGRANAHAN.

1. I will sing of my Re-deem-er And His won-drous love to me;
2. I will tell the wondrous sto-ry, How my lost es-tate to save,
3. I will praise my dear Re-deem-er, His tri-umph-ant pow'r I'll tell,
4. I will sing of my Re-deem-er, And His heav'n-ly love to me;

On the cru-el cross He suf-fered, From the curse to set me free.
In His boundless love and mer-cy, He the ran-som free-ly gave.
How the vic-to-ry He giv-eth O-ver sin, and death, and hell.
He from death to life hath bro't me Son, of God, with Him to be.

CHORUS.

Sing, oh! sing . . . . of my Re-deem-er, With His
Sing, oh! sing of my Re-deem-er, Sing, oh! sing of my Re-deem-er,

blood . . . . . He pur-chased me; . . . . . On the
He pur-chased me, With His blood He pur-chased me,

cross . . . . . He sealed my par-don, Paid the
He sealed my par-don, On the cross He sealed my par-don,

My Redeemer.

Repeat pp after last verse.

debt . . . . and made me free. . . . . . .

and made me free,

and made me free.

No. 71.   No, Not One!

Rev. JOHNSON OATMAN.

GEO. C. HUGG.

Slowly, and with great feeling.

1. There's not a friend like the low-ly Je-sus, No, not one! no, not one!
2. No friend like Him is so high and ho-ly, No, not one! no, not one!
3. There's not an hour that He is not near us, No, not one! no, not one!
4. Did ev-er saint find this friend for-sake him? No, not one! no, not one!
5. Was e'er a gift like the Sav-iour giv-en? No, not one! no, not one!

FINE.

None else could heal all our soul's dis-eas-es, No, not one! no, not one!
And yet no friend is so meek and low-ly, No, not one! no, not one!
No night so dark but His love can cheer us, No, not one! no, not one!
Or sin-ner find that He would not take Him? No, not one! no, not one!
Will He re-fuse us a home in heav-en? No, not one! no, not one!

D. S.—*There's not a friend like the low-ly Je-sus,* No, not one! no, not one!

CHORUS.

D. S.

Je-sus knows all a-bout our struggles, He will guide till the day is done;

No. 72. Jesus is Passing This Way.

Rev. E. A. Hoffman.   J. H. Tenney.

1. Is there a sin - ner a - wait - ing Mer - cy and par - don to - day?
2. Broth - er, the Mas - ter is wait - ing, Wait - ing to free - ly for - give;
3. Yes, He is com - ing to bless you While in con - tri - tion you bow:

Wel - come the news that we bring him: "Je - sus is pass - ing this way!"
Why not this mo - ment ac - cept Him, Trust in His grace and live?
Com - ing from sin to re - deem you, Read - y to save you now;

Com - ing in love and in mer - cy, Par - don and peace to be - stow,
He is so ten - der and pre - cious, He is so near you to - day;
Can you re - fuse the sal - va - tion Je - sus is of - fer - ing here?

Com - ing to save the poor sin - ner From His heart - an - guish and woe.
O - pen your heart to re - ceive Him, While He is pass - ing this way.
O - pen your heart to ad - mit Him, While He is com - ing so near.

Chorus.

Je - sus is passing this way, ... To - day, ... to - day, ...
Je - sus is pass - ing this way, To - day, is pass - ing to - day!

Jesus is Passing This Way.

While He is near, O be-lieve Him, O-pen your heart to re-ceive Him, for

Je-sus is pass-ing this way, ... Is pass-ing this way to-day.
this way,

No. 73. Fill Me Now.

E. H. STOKES, D. D.   J R. SWENEY.

1. Hov - er o'er me, Ho - ly Spir - it; Bathe my tremb-ling heart and brow;
2. Thou canst fill me, gra-cious Spir - it, Tho' I can-not tell Thee how;
3. I am weak-ness, full of weak-ness; At Thy sa-cred feet I bow;
4. Cleanse and comfort, bless and save me; Bathe, oh, bathe my heart and brow;

FINE.

Fill me with Thy hal-lowed pres-ence, Come, oh, come and fill me now.
But I need Thee, great-ly need Thee; Come, oh, come and fill me now.
Blest, di-vine, e - ter - nal Spir - it, Fill with pow'r, and fill me now.
Thou art com-fort-ing and sav - ing, Thou art sweet-ly fill-ing now.

D. S.—*Fill me with Thy hal-lowed pres-ence, Come, oh, come and fill me now*

CHORUS.   D. S.

Fill me now, fill me now, Je - sus, come and fill me now;

No. 74. Heavenly Sunlight.

Rev. H. J. ZELLEY.   G. H. COOK.

1. Walk-ing in sun-light, all of my jour-ney; O-ver the mount-ains,
2. Shad-ows a-round me, shad-ows a-bove me, Nev-er con-ceal my
3. In the bright sun-light, ev-er re-joic-ing, Press-ing my way to

thro' the deep vale; Je-sus has said I'll nev-er for-sake thee,
Sav-iour and Guide; He is the light, in Him is no dark-ness,
man-sions a-bove; Sing-ing His prais-es, glad-ly I'm walk-ing,

Prom-ise di-vine that nev-er can fail.
Ev-er I'm walk-ing close to His side.   Heav-en-ly sun-light,
Walk-ing in sun-light, sun-light of love.

CHORUS.

heav-en-ly sun-light; Flood-ing my soul with glo-ry di-vine; Hal-le-

lu-jah, I am re-joic-ing, Sing-ing His prais-es, Je-sus is mine.

No. 75.   Blessed Assurance.

FANNY J. CROSBY.   MRS. JOS. F. KNAPP.

1. Bless-ed as - sur - ance, Je - sus is   mine! Oh, what a fore - taste of
2. Per - fect sub - mis - sion, per - fect de - light, Vis - ions of rapt - ure now
3. Per - fect sub - mis - sion, all is at   rest, I   in my Sav - iour am

glo - ry   di - vine! Heir of sal - va - tion, pur-chase of   God, Born of His
burst on   my   sight, An-gels, de-scend - ing, bring from a - bove, Ech - oes of
hap - py and   blest, Watching and wait-ing, look-ing a - bove, Fill'd with His

CHORUS.

Spir - it, washed in His   blood.
mer - cy, whis-pers of   love.   This is my sto - ry, this is my
good - ness, lost in His   love.

song, Prais-ing my Sav - iour all the day   long; This is my

sto - ry, this is my song, Prais-ing my Sav - iour all the day long.

Used by permission.

No. 76. More and More I Need Thee

FANNY J. CROSBY.   W. H. DOANE.

1. More and more I need thee, Pre-cious Friend di-vine; More and
2. More and more I need thee, Thou, my all in all; More and
3. More and more I need thee, In temp-ta-tion's hour; More and
4. More and more I need thee, While the days go by; More and

more I need thee, In this heart of mine; Thou hast led me
more I need thee, Lest I faint and fall; I am weak and
more I need thee, Need thy keep-ing power; Let my soul up-
more I need thee, While the mo-ments fly; In thy se-cret

ev-er, Still my ref-uge be; Sav-iour, lov-ing Sav-iour, A-
help-less, Thou, my strength must be; Sav-iour, lov-ing Sav-iour, A-
lift-ed, Cling by faith to thee; Sav-iour, lov-ing Sav-iour, A-
pres-ence, Let my dwell-ing be; Sav-iour, lov-ing Sav-iour, A-

CHORUS.

bide with me.   More.... and more... I need thee, O   I
More and more, yes, more and more,

need thee! Sav-iour, lov-ing Sav-iour, A-bide with me.

Copyright, 1903, by W. H. Doane. Used by per.

No. 77. Onward, Christian Soldiers!

SABINE BARING-GOULD.   ARTHUR SULLIVAN.

1. On-ward, Christian sol - diers! Marching as to war, With the cross of
2. Like a might-y ar - my Moves the Church of God, Broth-ers, we are
3. Crowns and thrones may perish, King-doms rise and wane, But the Church of
4. On-ward, then, ye peo - ple! Join our hap-py throng, Blend with ours your

Je - sus Go - ing on - be - fore, Christ, the roy - al Mas - ter,
tread - ing Where the saints have trod; We are not di - vid - ed,
Je - sus Con-stant will re - main; Gates of hell can nev - er
voic - es In the tri-umph song; Glo - ry, laud and hon - or

Leads a-gainst the foe; For-ward in - to bat - tle, See, His ban-ners go!
All one bod - y we, One in hope and doc-trine, One in char - i - ty.
'Gainst that Church prevail, We have Christ's own promise, And that cannot fail.
Un - to Christ the King, This thro' countless a - ges Men and an-gels sing.

CHORUS.

On - ward, Chris-tian sol - diers! Marching as to war,

With the cross of Je - sus Go - ing on be - fore.

No. 78. 'Tis so Sweet to Trust in Jesus.

Mrs. Louisa M. R. Stead.   Wm. J. Kirkpatrick.

1. 'Tis so sweet to trust in Je - sus, Just to take Him at His Word;
2. O, how sweet to trust in Je - sus, Just to trust His cleans-ing blood;
3. Yes, 'tis sweet to trust in Je - sus, Just from sin and self to cease;
4. I'm so glad I learn'd to trust Thee, Pre-cious Je - sus, Sav - ior, Friend;

Just to rest up - on His prom-ise; Just to know, "Thus saith the Lord."
Just in sim - ple faith to plunge me 'Neath the heal - ing, cleansing flood.
Just from Je - sus sim - ply tak - ing Life, and rest, and joy, and peace.
And I know that Thou art with me, Wilt be with me to the end.

Chorus.

Je - sus, Je - sus, how I trust Him; How I've proved Him o'er and o'er,

Je - sus, Je - sus, Pre - cious Je - sus! O for grace to trust Him more

No. 79. Precious Name.

Mrs. Lydia Baxter.　　　　　　　　　　　　　　W. H. Doane.

1. Take the name of Je - sus with you, Child of sor - row and of woe;
2. Take the name of Je - sus ev - er, As a shield from ev - 'ry snare;
3. O the precious name of Je - sus! How it thrills our souls with joy
4. At the name of Je - sus bow - ing, Fall - ing prostrate at His feet,

It will joy and com-fort give, you, Take it then wher-e'er you go.
If temp-ta-tions 'round you gath - er, Breathe that ho - ly name in pray'r.
When His lov - ing arms re - ceive us, And His songs our tongues em-ploy!
King of kings in heav'n we'll crown Him, When our jour-ney is com - plete.

Chorus.

Pre - cious name, O how sweet!
Precious name, O how sweet!

Hope of earth and joy of heav'n, Pre - cious name,
Pre-cious name,

O how sweet! . . . Hope of earth and joy of heav'n.
O how sweet, how sweet!

No. 80. Blessed Jesus, Keep Me White.

P. P. B.

P. P. BILHORN.

1. Bless-ed Je - sus, Thou art mine, All I have is whol - ly Thine;
2. I am safe with - in the fold, All my cares on Thee are roll'd;
3. Pre-cious Je - sus, day by day, Keep me in the ho - ly way;

Thou dost dwell with - in my heart, Make me clean in ev - 'ry part.
I en - joy the sweet-est rest, For I'm lean - ing on Thy breast.
Keep my mind in per - fect peace, Ev - 'ry day my faith in-crease.

CHORUS.

white . . . . .

Bless-ed Je - - - - sus, keep me white, keep me white, Keep me
Bless - ed Je - sus, keep me white,

walk - - - - ing,

walking, keep me walk-ing in the light, ... All I have . . . is
Keep me walk-ing in the light, All I have

whol-ly Thine, ... Bless-ed Je - - - - sus, Thou art mine.
is whol - ly Thine, Bless - ed Je - sus,

Copyright, 1885, by P. P. Bilhorn. Used by per.

No. 81.   He Hideth My Soul.

FANNY J. CROSBY.   WM. J. KIRKPATRICK.

Allegretto.

1. A won - der - ful Sav - ior is   Je - sus my Lord,   A won - der - ful
2. A won - der - ful Sav - ior is   Je - sus my Lord,   He tak - eth my
3. With num - ber-less bless-ings each mo - ment He crowns, And fill'd with His
4. When cloth'd in His brightness trans-port - ed I rise   To meet Him in

Sav - ior to   me,   He hid - eth my soul   in the cleft of the rock, Where
bur - den a - way,   He hold-eth me up,   and I shall not be moved, He
full-ness di - vine,   I sing in my rapt - ure, oh, glo - ry to God For
clouds of the   sky,   His per-fect sal - va - tion, His won - der-ful love, I'll

CHORUS.

riv - ers of pleasure I   see.
giveth me strength as my   day.   He hid - eth my soul   in the cleft of the rock,
such a Re-deemer as   mine.
shout with the millions on   high.

That shadows   a dry, thirst-y   land; He hid - eth my life   in the depths of His

love, And cov - ers me there with His hand, And cov - ers me there with His hand.

No. 82.

Sing On.

CARRIE M. WILSON.   JNO. R. SWENEY, By per.

1. Sing on, ye joy - ful pil - grims, Nor think the mo - ments long;
2. Sing on, ye joy - ful pil - grims, While here on earth we stay;
3. Sing on, ye joy - ful pil - grims, The time will not be long;

My faith is heav'n-ward ris - ing, With ev - 'ry tune - ful song;
Let songs of home and Je - sus Be - guile each fleet - ing day;
Till in our Fa - ther's king - dom We swell a no - bler song;

Lo! on the mount of bless - ing, The glo - rious mount I stand.
Sing on the grand old sto - ry Of His re-deem - ing love;
Where those we love are wait - ing To greet us on the shore,

And look - ing o - ver Jor - dan, I see the prom - ised land!
The ev - er - last - ing cho - rus That fills the realms a - bove.
We'll meet be - yond the riv - er, Where surg - es roll no more.

CHORUS.

Sing on; O bliss-ful mu - sic, With ev - 'ry note you raise,

Sing On.

My heart is fill'd with rapt - ure, My soul is lost in praise.

Sing on; O bliss-ful mu - sic, With ev - 'ry note you raise,
Sing on; bliss - ful, bliss - ful mu - sic,

My heart is fill'd with rapt - ure, My soul is lost in praise.

No. 83. Blest Be the Tie.

JOHN FAWCETT.   HANS GEORG NAEGELI.

1. Blest be the tie that binds Our heart in Chris - tian love; The
2. Be - fore our Fa - ther's throne We pour our ar - dent pray'rs: Our
3. We share our mu - tual woes, Our mu - tual bur - dens bear; And
4. When we a - sun - der part, It gives us in - ward pain; But

fel - low - ship of kin - dred minds Is like to that a - bove.
fears, our hopes; our aims are one Our com - forts and our tears.
oft - en for each oth - er flows The sym - pa - thiz - ing tear.
we shall still be joined in heart, And hope to meet a - gain.

No. 84. Seek Ye First the Kingdom.

E. E. HEWITT.

JNO. R. SWENEY.

1. Seek ye first the king - dom; Not the things of earth, Price-less are the treas-ures Of im-mor-tal worth. Like a flit - ting shad - ow, Time will pass a - way, But the heav'nly rich - es Change not, nor de - cay.

2. Seek ye first the king - dom; Ev - er - last-ing love Woes you to the bless-ings From the land a - bove. Par-don and re - new - al, Righteous-ness and peace, Grace for ev - 'ry tri - al, Joys that nev - er cease.

3. Seek ye first the king - dom; Seek the "Gift of God;" 'Tis the Saviour's of - fer, Purchased by His blood. Seek ye first His glo - ry; Be it life's sweet aim, Him to serve and hon - or, Trust-ing in His name.

CHORUS.

Seek ye first the kingdom; 'Tis the Master's voice; In His precious prom-ise

Ev - er-more re - joice. "All things else," His word is true, "Shall be ad - ded

Seek Ye First.

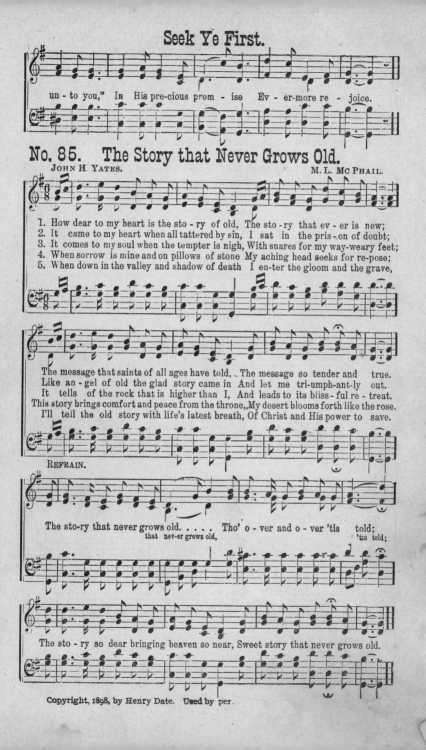

un - to you," In His pre-cious prom - ise Ev - er-more re - joice.

No. 85.   The Story that Never Grows Old.

JOHN H. YATES.   M. L. McPHAIL.

1. How dear to my heart is the sto - ry of old, The sto - ry that ev - er is new;
2. It   came to my heart when all tattered by sin, I sat   in   the pris - on of doubt;
3. It comes to my soul when the tempter is nigh, With snares for my way-weary feet;
4. When sorrow is mine and on pillows of stone My aching head seeks for re-pose;
5. When down in the valley and shadow of death   I en-ter the gloom and the grave,

The message that saints of all ages have told, The message so tender and   true.
Like an - gel of old the glad story came in And let me tri-umph-ant-ly   out.
It   tells   of the rock that is higher than I, And leads to its bliss - ful re - treat.
This story brings comfort and peace from the throne, My desert blooms forth like the rose.
I'll   tell   the old   story with life's latest breath, Of Christ and His power to   save.

REFRAIN.

The sto - ry that never grows old. . . . .   Tho' o - ver and o - ver 'tis   told;
       that nev-er grows old,   'tis told;

The sto - ry so dear bringing heaven so near, Sweet story that never grows old.

No. 86.   Trust and Obey.

Rev. J. H. SAMMIS.   D. B. TOWNER.

1. When we walk with the Lord   In the light of His Word, What a glo - ry He
2. Not a shad-ow can rise,   Not a cloud in the skies, But His smile quickly
3. Not a bur-den we bear,   Not a sor-row we share, But our toil He doth
4. But we nev-er can prove   The de-lights of His love Un - til all on the
5. Then in fel-low-ship sweet   We will sit at His feet, Or we'll walk by His

sheds on our way! While we do His good will, He a-bides with us
drives it a - way; Not a doubt nor a fear, Not a sigh nor a
rich - ly re - pay; Not a grief nor a loss, Not a frown nor a
al - tar we lay; For the fa - vor He shows, And the joy He be-
side in the way; What He says we will do, Where He sends we will

CHORUS.

still, And with all who will trust and o - bey.
tear Can a - bide while we trust and o - bey.
cross, But is blest, if we trust and o - bey. Trust and o - bey, For there's
stows, Are for all who will trust and o - bey.
go, Nev-er fear, on - ly trust and o - bey.

no oth-er way To be hap - py in Je - sus But to trust and o - bey.

No. 87. Labor On.

Dr. C. R. BLACKALL. W. H, DOANE.

Spirited.

1. In the har-vest field there is work to do, For the
2. Crowd the gar-ner well with the sheaves all bright, Let the
3. In the glean-er's path may be rich re-ward, Tho' the
4. Lo! the Har-vest Home in the realms a-bove Shall be

grain is ripe, and the reap-ers few, And the Mas-ter's voice bids the
song be glad, and the heart be light, Fill the pre-cious hours, ere the
time seems long, and the la-bor hard; For the Mas-ter's joy, with His
gained by each who has toiled and strove; When the Mas-ter's voice, in His

work-ers true Heed the call that He gives to-day.
shades of night Take the place of the gold-en day.
chos-en shared, Drives the gloom from the dark-est day.
words of love, Calls a-way to e-ter-nal day.

CHORUS.

La-bor on, la-bor on, Keep the bright reward in view, For the
La-bor on, la-bor on,

Mas-ter has said, He will strength renew, La-bor on till the close of day.

No. 88. One More Day's Work for Jesus.

ANNA WARNER.　　　　　　　　　　　　　　　　ROBERT LOWRY.

1. One more day's work for Je - sus, One less of life for me;
2. One more day's work for Je - sus; How glo - rious is my King!
3. One more day's work for Je - sus; How sweet the work has been,
4. One more day's work for Je - sus— O yes, a wea - ry day;
5. O bless - ed work for Je - sus! O rest at Je - sus' feet!

But heav'n is near - er, And Christ is dear - er, Than yes - ter - day, to
'Tis joy, not du - ty, To speak His beau - ty: My soul mounts on the
To tell the sto - ry, To show the glo - ry Where Christ's flock en - ter
But heav'n shines clearer, And rest comes nearer, At each step of the
There toil seems pleasure, My wants are treasure, And pain for Him is

me; His love and light Fill all my soul to - night.
wing At the mere thought How Christ my life has bought.
in! How it did shine In this poor heart of mine!
way; And Christ in all— Be - fore His face I fall.
sweet; Lord, if I may, I'll serve an - oth - er day.

CHORUS.

One more day's work for Je - sus, One more day's work for Je - sus,

One more day's work for Je - sus, One less of life for me.

No. 89. Keep on the Sunny Side of Life.

ADA BLENKHORN. J. HOWARD ENTWISLE.

1. There's a dark and a troub-led side of life; There's a bright and a
2. Tho' the storm in its fu - ry break to - day, Crush - ing hopes that we
3. Let us greet with a song of hope each day, Tho' the mo-ments be

sun - ny side, too; Tho' we meet with the dark-ness and strife, The
cher-ished so dear; Storm and cloud will in time pass a - way, The
cloud - y or fair; Let us trust in our Sav - iour al - way, Who

CHORUS.

sun - ny side we al - so may view.
sun again will shine bright and clear. Keep on the sun-ny side, Al-ways on the
keep-eth ev - 'ry one in His care.

sun-ny side, Keep on the sun-ny side of life; It will help us ev - 'ry day,

It will brighten all the way, If we keep on the sun-ny side of life.

No. 90. Wilt Thou Be Made Whole?

W. J. K.

WM. J. KIRKPATRICK.

1. Hear the footsteps of Je-sus, He is now pass-ing by, Bear-ing balm for the
2. 'Tis the voice of that Sav-iour, Whose mer-ci-ful call Free-ly of-fers sal-
3. Are you halting and struggling, O'er-pow'red by your sin, While the wa-ters are
4. Bless-ed Sav-iour, as-sist us To rest on Thy word; Let the soul-heal-ing

wound-ed, Healing all who ap-ply; As He spake to the suff-'rer Who
va-tion To one and to all; He is now beck'ning to Him Each
troub-led, Can you not en-ter in? Lo! the Sav-iour stands waiting To
pow-er On us now be out-pour'd: Wash a-way ev-'ry sin-spot, Take

FINE.

lay at the pool, He is say-ing this moment, "Wilt thou be made whole?"
sin-taint-ed soul, And lov-ing-ly ask-ing, "Wilt thou be made whole?"
strengthen your soul, He is ear-nest-ly pleading. "Wilt thou be made whole?"
per-fect con-trol, Say to each trust-ing spir-it, "Thy faith makes thee whole."

D. S.—cleansing waves roll: Step in-to the cur-rent And thou shalt be whole.

CHORUS.

Wilt thou be made whole? Wilt thou be made whole? O come, wea-ry

D. S.

suf-f'rer, O come, sin-sick soul; See the life-stream is flow-ing, See, the

No. 91. Battle Hymn of the Republic.

JULIA WARD HOWE.   Arr.

1. Mine eyes have seen the glo - ry of the com - ing of the Lord; He is
2. I have seen Him in the watch-fires of a hun-dred cir-cling camps; They have
3. He has sounded forth the trump-et that shall nev - er call re - treat; He is
4. In the beau - ty of the lil - ies, Christ was born a-cross the sea, With a

trampling out the vint-age where the grapes of wrath are stored; He hath loosed the
build-ed Him an al - tar in the eve - ning dews and damps; I have read His
sift - ing out the hearts of men be - fore His judgment-seat; Oh, be swift, my
glo - ry in His bos - om that trans-fig - ures you and me; As He died to

fate-ful light-ning of His ter - ri-ble, swift sword, His truth is marching on.
righteous sen-tence by the dim and flar - ing lamps, His day is marching on.
soul, to an - swer Him! be ju - bi-lant, my feet! Our God is marching on.
make men ho - ly, let us die to make men free, While God is marching on.

CHORUS.

Glo - ry, glo - ry, hal - le - lu - jah! Glo - ry, glo - ry, hal - le - lu jah!

Glo - ry, glo - ry, hal - le - lu - jah! His truth is marching on.

No. 92. There shall be Showers of Blessing.

EL. NATHAN.   JAMES McGRANAHAN.

1. "There shall be show-ers of bless-ing:" This is the prom-ise of love;
2. "There shall be show-ers of bless-ing"—Pre-cious re-viv-ing a-gain;
3. "There shall be show-ers of bless-ing:" Send them up-on us, O Lord;
4. "There shall be show-ers of bless-ing:" Oh that to-day they might fall,

There shall be sea-sons re-fresh-ing, Sent from the Sav-ior a-bove.
O-ver the hills and the val-leys, Sound of a-bun-dance of rain.
Grant to us now a re-fresh-ing; Come, and now hon-or Thy word.
Now as to God we're con-fess-ing, Now as on Je-sus we call!

CHORUS.

Show - ers of bless-ing, Show-ers of bless-ing we need;
Show - ers, show-ers

Mer - cy-drops 'round us are fall-ing, But for the show-ers we plead.

No. 93. Abiding In Christ.

A. M. STARKWEATHER. JAS. M. BLACK.

1. I'm a-bid-ing in Christ, where no sea bil-lows roll, Where the
2. I'm a-bid-ing in Christ, and His love is so sweet, For it
3. I'm a-bid-ing in Christ, as the branch in the vine: And new
4. O, that ha-ven of rest from the temp-est is found In a-

tem-pest is hushed to a calm; 'Tis a ha-ven or rest for the
fills me with peace ev-'ry day; And I find in His pres-ence a
strength He im-parts ev-'ry hour; As I feed on the Word and I
bid-ing in Christ's blessed will, Where no e-vil can come, and no

storm-driv-en soul And the wea-ry may here find a balm.
bless-ed re-treat From the tri-als and toils of the way.
drink of the wine I am kept by His won-der-ful pow'r.
dis-cord of sound Where the waves hear His voice and are still.

CHORUS.

I'm a-bid-ing, (I'm a-bid-ing,) a-bid-ing in Christ, And He sat-is-fies my soul ev-'ry

day, (ev-'ry day,) I'm a-bid-ing, a-bid-ing in Christ, ev'ry day, all the way.

No. 94. I Know He's Mine.

Rev. JOHNSON OATMAN, Jr.　　　　　　　　　　B. FRANK BUTTS.

1. There's One a-bove all earth-ly friends Whose love all earth-ly love transcends,
2. He's mine be-cause He died for me, He saved my soul, He set me free;
3. He's mine be-cause He's in my heart, And nev-er, nev-er will we part;
4. Some day up-on the streets of gold Mine eyes His glo-ry shall be-hold,

It is my Lord and Christ di-vine, My Lord, be-cause I know He's mine.
With joy I wor-ship at His shrine And cry, "Praise God, I know He's mine."
Just as the branch is to the vine I'm joined to Christ; I know He's mine.
Then, while His arms a-round me twine, I'll cry for joy, "I know He's mine."

CHORUS.

I know He's mine, ... this friend so dear . . . . He lives with
I know He's mine,　　　　this friend so dear,

me . . . . . . He's ev-er near; . . . . . . Ten thou-sand
He lives with me,　　　　He's ev-er near,

charms . . . . around Him shine, ... And best of all, I know He's mine.
Ten thousand charms　　around Him shine,

No. 95. O Think of the Home Over There.

D. W. C. HUNTINGTON.   T. C. O'KANE.

1. O, think of a home o-ver there, By the side of the riv-er of light,
2. O, think of the friends o-ver there, Who be-fore us the journey have trod,
3. My Sav-ior is now o-ver there, There my kindred and friends are at rest;
4. I'll soon be at home o-ver there, For the end of my jour-ney I see;

Over there,

Where the saints all immor-tal and fair, Are robed in their garments of white.
Of the songs that they breathe on the air, In their home in the pal-ace of God.
Then a-way from my sorrow and care, Let me fly to the land of the blest.
Ma - ny dear to my heart o-ver there, Are watching and waiting for me.

O-ver there.

REFRAIN.

O - ver there,   o - ver there,   O, think of the home o - ver there,
O - ver there,   o - ver there,   O, think of the friends o-ver there,
O - ver there,   o - ver there,   My Sav-ior is now o - ver there,
O - ver there,   o - ver there,   I'll soon be at home o - ver there,

O - ver there,   o - ver there,   o - ver there,

O - ver there,   o - ver there, o-ver there, O, think of a home o - ver there.
O - ver there,   o - ver there, o-ver there, O, think of the friends o - ver there.
O - ver there,   o - ver there, o-ver there, My Sav-ior is now o - ver there.
O - ver there,   o - ver there, o-ver there, I'll soon be at home o - ver there.

O - ver there,

No. 96. I Have Found a Friend Indeed.

JOHNSON OATMAN, JR.

WM. J. KIRKPATRICK.

1. I have found a friend indeed, Who supplies my ev-'ry need, My Sav-ior,
2. He has washed me from all sin, He has made me pure with-in, My Sav-ior,
3. When I have a heav-y trial, He be-stows on me a smile, My Sav-ior,
4. He's prepared a home for me, O-ver by the crys-tal sea, My Sav-ior,

precious Sav-ior; With the eye of faith sublime, I can see Him all the time,
precious Sav-ior; He hath made my spir-it whole, Spoken peace to my poor soul,
precious Sav-ior; And I find no oth-er rest, Like the ha-ven of His breast,
precious Sav-ior; When life's fit-ful dream is o'er, I will dwell up-on that shore,

CHORUS.

And He's with me all the way.
And He bless-es me each day. Hal-le-lu-jah! I am walk-ing with my
For a pres-ent help is He.
Thro' a bright e-ter-ni-ty.

I am

Sav - ior, My dear Sav-ior, precious Sav-ior, And He keeps me in His

walking with my Sav-ior   My dear Sav-ior,   precious Sav-ior, He

per-fect love and fa - vor, And I nev-er have to walk a-lone.

His per-fect love and fa-vor.

No. 97. Lead Me, Savior.

F. M. D.

FRANK M. DAVIS.

With expression.

1. Sav - ior, lead me, lest I stray, Gen - tly lead me all the way, I am safe when by Thy side, I would in Thy love a - bide.
2. Thou the ref - uge of my soul, When life's storm-y bil - lows roll, I am safe when Thou art nigh, All my hopes on Thee re - ly.
3. Sav - ior, lead me, then at last, When the storm of life is past, To the land of end - less day, Where all tears are wiped a - way.

CHORUS.

Lead me, lead me, Sav - ior, lead me, lest I stray; . . .

rit e dim.

Gently down the stream of time, Lead me, Sav-ior, all the way.

Never Alone.

THEODORE.

Arr. by T. C. O'KANE.

1. "Lo! I am with you al - way," I hear the Sav-ior say; To save, and
2. When fiercely storms are raging, On Him I call in pray'r. He folds His
3. When skies a-bove are shin - ing, And ev - 'ry-thing is bright; When peace is
4. "Lo! I am with you al - way," I hear the Sav-ior say, And hear-ing,

guide and keep me Thro' all my pil - grim way; Be strong, my heart, and
arms a - round me And guards with tend'rest care; He light-ens up my
"like a riv - er," All tend - ing to de - light; When in the "si - lent
glad - ly trav - el And trust Him day by day: When in the heav'nly

jour - ney, With ceaseless vig - or, on, And heark-en to His prom - ise,
path - way With flash - es from His throne, And speaks a-bove the tem - pest,
watch - es," When dearest friends are gone; In shade and shine He whispers,
man - sions Prepared for all His own, He'll ver - i - fy His prom - ise,

CHORUS.

I nev - er will leave thee a-lone," No, nev - er a - lone, ...
No, nev - er, no nev - er a-lone,

No, nev - er a - lone, . . . He's prom - ised to be with me, He
No, nev - er, no nev - er a-lone,

Never Alone.

nev-er will leave me a-lone; Nev-er will leave me a-lone.

a-lone.

No. 99. Face to Face.

Mrs. Frank A. Breck. Grant Colfax Tullar.

1. Face to face with Christ my Sav-ior, Face to face—what will it be?
2. On-ly faint-ly now I see Him, With the dark-ling veil be-tween,
3. What re-joic-ing in His pres-ence, When are ban-ished grief and pain;
4. Face to face! oh, bliss-ful mo-ment! Face to face—to see and know;

When with rapt-ure I be-hold Him, Je-sus Christ who died for me.
But a bless-ed day is com-ing, When His glo-ry shall be seen.
When the crook-ed ways are straightened, And the dark things shall be plain.
Face to face with my Re-deem-er, Je-sus Christ who loves me so.

Chorus.

Face to face shall I be-hold Him, Far be-yond the star-ry sky;

Face to face in all His glo-ry, I shall see Him by and by!

No. 100. We're Marching to Zion.

Rev. I. Watts.   Rev. R. Lowry.

1. Come, ye that love the Lord, And let your joys be known; Join in a
2. Let those re - fuse to sing Who nev - er knew our God; But chil - dren
3. The hill of Zi - on yields A thou-sand sa - cred sweets, Be - fore we
4. Then let our songs a-bound, And ev -'ry tear be dry; We're march-ing

song with sweet ac - cord, Join in a song with sweet ac - cord,
of the heav'n - ly King, But chil - dren of the heav'n - ly King,
reach the heav'n - ly fields, Be - fore we reach the heav'n - ly fields,
thro' Im - man - uel's ground, We're march - ing thro' Im - man - uel's ground,

And thus sur - round the throne, And thus sur-round the throne.
May speak their joys a - broad, May speak their joys a - broad.
Or walk the gold - en streets, Or walk the gold - en streets.
To fair - er worlds on high, To fair - er worlds on high.
And thus sur-round the throne, And thus sur - round the throne.

CHORUS.

We're march - ing to Zi - on, Beau - ti - ful, beau - ti - ful Zi - on, We're
We're march - ing on to Zi - on,

march - ing up-ward to Zi - on, The beau - ti - ful cit - y of God.
Zi - on, Zi - on,

No. 101. My Soul is Anchored.

Mrs. Annie S. Hawks.   Jas. M. Black.

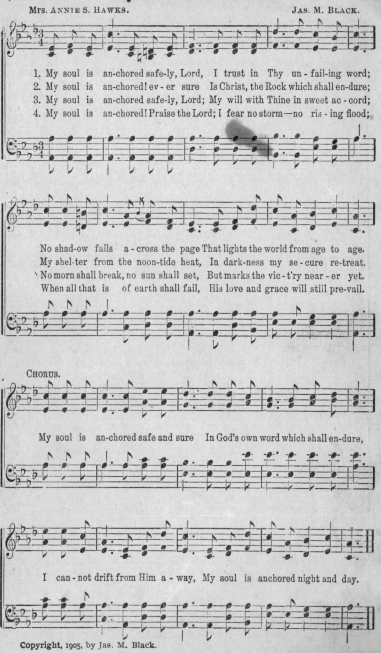

1. My soul is an-chored safe-ly, Lord, I trust in Thy un-fail-ing word;
2. My soul is an-chored! ev-er sure Is Christ, the Rock which shall en-dure;
3. My soul is an-chored safe-ly, Lord; My will with Thine in sweet ac-cord;
4. My soul is an-chored! Praise the Lord; I fear no storm—no ris-ing flood;

No shad-ow falls a-cross the page That lights the world from age to age.
My shel-ter from the noon-tide heat, In dark-ness my se-cure re-treat.
No morn shall break, no sun shall set, But marks the vic-t'ry near-er yet.
When all that is of earth shall fail, His love and grace will still pre-vail.

CHORUS.

My soul is an-chored safe and sure In God's own word which shall en-dure,

I can-not drift from Him a-way, My soul is anchored night and day.

No. 102.   The Glad Reunion By and By.

Rev. W. C. Martin.   Jas. M. Black.

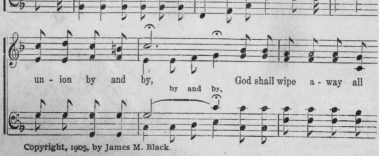

1. There will be a glad re-un-ion by and by, Sev-ered hearts will be u-
2. Brightly gleams this Star of hope when suns go down, Ev - 'ry child of God shall
3. We can al-most see that bright and shin-ing land, Where the chil-dren of the

nit - ed soon on high; Friend with friend a - gain shall meet, Joy and
wear a star-ry crown; Here we la - bor and we pray, Here our
King in glo - ry stand; Where with rapt - ured hearts they sing Of their

glad-ness be re-plete In that land where sor-row nev-er dims the eye.
treas-ures fade a - way, But up yon-der wait-eth hon-or and re-nown.
Sav - ior, Lord and King, Who redeemed and led them on-ward by His hand

CHORUS.

O the glad re - un-ion by and by,
by and by,
O the glad re-

un - ion by and by,
by and by,
God shall wipe a - way all

Copyright, 1905, by James M. Black.

The Glad Reunion By and By.

tears from ev - 'ry eye,   At   the   glad   re - un - ion   by   and   by.

No. 103.   He's Everything to Me.

Mrs. P. P. STRAWINSKI.

J. J. JENNINGS.

1. Since Je - sus came in - to my soul to live, He's ev - 'ry-thing to me,
2. No more shall I grieve the dear Sav-ior's love, He's ev - 'ry-thing to me;
3. The darkness of sin has all passed a - way, He's ev - 'ry-thing to me;
4. O,   glo - ry   to   Je - sus, my Priest and King, He's ev - 'ry-thing to me;

And now un - to Him all my heart I give, He's ev - 'ry-thing to me. . .
He whispers sweet tidings from heav'n a - bove, He's ev - 'ry-thing to me. . .
The Mas-ter has come and will ev - er stay, He's ev - 'ry-thing to me. . .
Tri - um-phant, I nev - er can cease to sing, He's ev - 'ry-thing to me. . .

REFRAIN.

He's ev - 'ry-thing to me, . . .   He's ev - 'ry-thing to me, . . .
to me.   to me,

Christ Je - sus reigns with - in   my heart, He's ev - 'ry-thing to   me.

No. 104. Beautiful Robes.

E. E. HEWITT.

W. J. KIRKPATRICK.

Noot too fast.

1. We shall walk with Him in white, In that coun-try pure and bright,
2. We shall walk with Him in white, Where faith yields to bliss-ful sight,
3. We shall walk with Him in white, By the fount-ains of de-light,

Where shall en-ter naught that may de-file; Where the day beam ne'er declines,
When the beau-ty of the King we see; Hold-ing converse full and sweet,
Where the Lamb His ransomed ones shall lead; For His blood shall wash each stain,

For the bless-ed light that shines Is the glo-ry of the Saviour's smile.
In a fel-low-ship com-plete; Wak-ing songs of ho-ly mel-o-dy.
Till no spot of sin re-main, And the soul for-ev-er-more is freed.

CHORUS.

Beau - ti-ful robes, ... Beau - ti-ful robes, ...
Beau-ti-ful robes, beau-ti-ful robes, Beau-ti-ful robes, beau-ti-ful robes,

Beau - ti-ful robes, we then shall wear; ...
Beau-ti-ful robes, we then shall wear, Beau-ti-ful robes we then shall wear;

Beautiful Robes.

Gar - ments of light, ... Love - ly and bright, ...
Gar-ments of light, gar-ments of light, Love-ly and bright, love-ly and bright,

Walk - ing with Je - sus in white, Beau - ti - ful robes we shall wear.

No. 105.   I Need Thee Every Hour.

Mrs. Annie E, Hawkes.   Rev. Robert Lowry.

1. I need Thee ev-'ry hour, Most gra - cious Lord; No ten - der voice like
2. I need Thee ev-'ry hour, Stay Thou near by; Temp - ta - tions lose their
3. I need Thee ev-'ry hour, In joy or pain; Come quick-ly and a-
4, I need Thee ev-'ry hour; Teach me Thy will; And Thy rich prom-is-
5. I need Thee ev-'ry hour, Most Ho - ly One; O make me Thine in-

Refrain.

Thine Can peace af - ford.
pow'r When Thou art nigh.
bide, Or life is vain.   I need Thee, O I need Thee, Ev - 'ry hour I
es In me ful - fill.
deed, Thou bless - ed Son!

need Thee; O bless me now, my Sav - ior, I come to Thee.

No. 106. My Saviour is With Me.

ADA BLENKHORN.   L. F. J. Arr. by JAS. M. BLACK.

1. My Sav-iour is with me, wher-ev - er I go, In dark-ness and
2. His life - giv - ing words faith and cour-age re - new, They fall on my
3. My Sav - iour is with me the tho't, O how sweet! How bless-ed the

dan - ger the way He doth show; When storms rage a-round me, and
spir - it re-fresh-ing as dew; On heav-en - ly man - na my
les - sons I learn at His feet; How pre-cious the wis - dom His

sor-rows in - crease, He still-eth the temp-est and giv - eth me peace.
scul He doth feed, In paths of His choos-ing my steps He doth lead.
love doth im - part, With joy and de - vo - tion it fill - eth my heart.

CHORUS.

I'll trust in my Sav - iour, what-ev - er be - tide, I know all my

foot-steps He safe-ly will guide; I know He will guard me with ten-der-est

My Saviour is With Me.

love, Un-til I shall en-ter His glo-ry a-bove.

No. 107. Day is Dying in the West.

MARY A. LATHBURY.   WILLIAM E. SHERWIN.

1. Day is dy-ing in the west; Heav'n is touch-ing earth with rest; Wait and
2. While the deep'ning shadows fall, Heart of Love, en-fold-ing all, Thro' the
3. When for ev-er from our sight Pass the stars, the day, the night, Lord of

wor-ship while the night Sets her eve-ning lamps a-light Thro' all the sky.
glo-ry and the grace Of the stars that veil Thy face, Our hearts as-cend.
an-gels, on our eyes Let e-ter-nal morning rise, And shad-ows end.

REFRAIN. *pp*

Ho-ly, Ho-ly, Ho-ly, Lord God of Hosts! Heav'n and earth are

ff

full of Thee; Heav'n and earth are prais-ing Thee, O Lord Most High!

No. 108.   Stepping in the Light.

L. H. EDMUNDS.   WM. J. KIRKPATRICK.

1. Try-ing   to walk in   the steps of   the Sav-iour, Try - ing   to fol - low our
2. Pressing more closely   to Him who is lead-ing, When we are tempted to
3. Walking   in foot-steps of gen - tle   forbearance, Foot-steps of faith-ful-ness,
4. Try-ing   to walk in   the steps of   the Sav-iour, Upward, still upward we'll

Sav - iour and King;   Shap - ing our lives by His bless - ed   ex-am - ple,
turn from the way;   Trust-ing the arm that is strong to   de-fend us,
mer - cy, and love,   Look-ing   to Him for the grace free - ly promised.
fol - low our guide,   When we shall see Him, "the King in His beau-ty,"

CHORUS.

Hap-py, how hap-py, the songs that we bring!
Hap-py, how hap-py, our prais-es each day!   How beauti-ful to walk in the
Hap-py, how hap-py, our jour-ney a-bove!
Hap-py, how hap-py, our place at His side!

steps of   the Sav-iour, Step-ping in   the light, Step-ping in   the light; How

beau-ti - ful to walk in   the steps of   the Sav-iour, Led in paths of light!

No. 109. My Mother is Praying for Me.

MAY AGNES OSGOOD.   Rev. J. H. WEBER.

SOLO.

1. I knelt by my moth-er, her hand on my head, And ut-tered my
2. In dark-ness and sin I have wandered a-way, Nor tried from temp-
3. I'm wea-ry of sin-ning; I turn to the cross, And its light shin-ing

pray'r at her knee; Now far, far a-way from her side I have stray'd,
ta-tion to flee; But down in my heart I could nev-er for-get
o'er me I see; I'll go to my Sav-ior and thank Him a-gain

CHORUS.

But my moth-er is pray-ing for me.
That my moth-er was pray-ing for me. My moth-er is pray-ing for
That a moth-er was pray-ing for me.

me, . . . My moth-er is praying for me, . . . For sure-ly I
for me,   for me,

know that wher-ev-er I go My mother is pray-ing for me. . . .
for me

No. 110. God Be With You.

Rev. J. E. Rankin, D. D.   W. G. Tomer.

1. God be with you till we meet a - gain, By His coun-sels guide, up-
2. God be with you till we meet a - gain, 'Neath his wings se - cure - ly
3. God be with you till we meet a - gain, When life's per - ils thick con-
4. God be with you till we meet a - gain, Keep love's ban-ner float - ing

hold   you,   With his sheep se - cure - ly fold   you;
hide   you,   Dai - ly man - na still pro - vide   you;
found   you,   Put His lov - ing arms a - round   you;
o'er   you,   Smite death's threat'ning wave be - fore   you;

CHORUS.

God be with you till we meet a - gain. Till we meet,   till we
                                          Till we meet, till we

meet,   Till we meet at Je - sus' feet,   Till we
meet, a - gain,   Till we meet,

meet,   till we meet,   God be with you till we meet a-gain.
till we meet, till we meet, a - gain,

No. 111. Just as I Am.

C. Elliott.   Wm. B. Bradbury.

1. Just as I am, with-out one plea, But that Thy blood was shed for me,
2. Just as I am, and wait ing not To rid my soul of one dark blot,
3. Just as I am, though tossed a-bout With many a con-flict, many a doubt,
4. Just as I am—Thou wilt re-ceive, Wilt welcome, par-don, cleanse, re-lieve;
5. Just as I am—Thy love unknown, Hath bro-ken ev-'ry bar-rier down;

And that Thou bidd'st me come to Thee, O Lamb of God, I come! I come!
To Thee whose blood can cleanse each spot, O Lamb of God, I come! I come!
Fightings with-in, and fears with-out, O Lamb of God, I come! I come!
Be-cause Thy promise I be-lieve, O Lamb of God, I come! I come!
Now to be Thine, yea, Thine a-lone, O Lamb of God, I come! I come!

No. 112. The Call for Reapers.

J. O. Thompson.   J. B. O. Clemm.

1. Far and near the fields are teem-ing With the fields of ripened grain;
2. Send them forth with morn's first beaming; Send them in the noontide's glare;
3. O thou, whom thy Lord is send-ing, Gath-er now the sheaves of gold;

Far and near their gold is gleaming, O'er the sun-ny slope and plain.
When the sun's last rays are gleaming, Bid them gath-er ev-'ry-where.
Heav'nward then at eve-ning wend-ing, Thou shalt come with joy un-told.

D.S.—Send them now the sheaves to gath-er, Ere the har-vest time pass by.

CHORUS.   D.S.

Lord of har-vest, send forth reap-ers! Hear us, Lord, to Thee we cry;

No. 113.   There is a Fountain.

WILLIAM COWPER.   Dr. LOWELL MASON.

1. There is a fountain filled with blood, Drawn from Im - man-uel's veins;
2. The dy - ing thief re-joiced to see   That fount-ain in his day;
3. Dear dy - ing Lamb, Thy precious blood Shall nev - er lose its power,
4. E'er since, by faith, I saw the stream Thy flow - ing wounds sup- ply,
5. Then, in a no - bler, sweet-er song, I'll sing Thy pow'r to save,

And sin - ners plunged beneath that flood, Lose all their guilt y stains,
And there may I, though vile as he,   Wash all my sins a - way,
Till all the ransomed Church of God Be saved, to sin no more,
Re - deem -ing love has been my theme, And shall be till I die,
When this poor lisp-ing stamm'ring tongue Lies si - lent in the grave,

Lose all their guilt- y   stains,   Lose all their guilt- y stains.
Wash all my sins a - way,   Wash all my sins a - way.
Be saved, to sin no more, Be saved, to sin no more.
And shall be till I   die,   And shall be till I die.
Lies si - lent in the   grave, Lies si - lent in the grave.

No. 114.   There's a Wideness.

FREDERICK W. FABER.   LIZZIE J. TOURJEE.

1. There's a wide-ness in God's mer-cy, Like the wide-ness of the sea;
2. There is wel-come for the sin - ner, And more grac-es for the good;
3. For the love of God is broad-er Than the measure of man's mind;
4. If our love were but more sim-ple, We should take Him at His word;

There's a kind - ness in His jus -tice, Which is more than lib - er - ty.
There is mer - cy with the Sav-iour; There is heal-ing in His blood.
And the heart of the E - ter - nal   Is most won-der - ful- ly kind.
And our lives would be all sun-shine In the sweetness of our Lord.

No. 115. Work, for the Night is Coming.

SIDNEY DYER. LOWELL MASON.

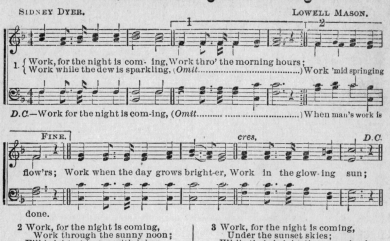

1. {Work, for the night is com- ing, Work thro' the morning hours;
Work while the dew is sparkling, (*Omit*.......................................)Work 'mid springing

D.C.—Work for the night is com-ing, (*Omit*.......... ....)When man's work is

flow'rs; Work when the day grows bright-er, Work in the glow-ing sun;

done.

2 Work, for the night is coming,
Work through the sunny noon;
Fill brightest hours with labor,
Rest comes sure and soon.
Give every flying minute
Something to keep in store;
Work, for the night is coming,
When man works no more.

3 Work, for the night is coming,
Under the sunset skies;
While their bright tints are glowing,
Work, for daylight flies.
Work till the last beam fadeth,
Fadeth to shine no more;
Work while the night is darkening,
When man's work is o'er.

No. 116.   My Jesus, as Thou Wilt.

BENJAMIN SCHMOLKE. Tr. C. M. VON WEBER. Arr.

1. My Je - sus, as Thou wilt! O may Thy will be mine; In - to Thy hand of love
2. My Je - sus, as Thou wilt! Tho' seen thro' many a tear, Let not my star of hope
3. My Je - sus, as Thou wilt! All shall be well with me, Each changing future scene

I would my all re - sign; Thro' sor - row or thro' joy, Con-duct me
Grow dim or dis-ap - pear; Since Thou on earth hast wept, And sorrowed
I glad - ly trust with Thee; Straight to my home a-bove I trav-el

as Thine own, And help me still to say, "My Lord, Thy will be done."
oft a-lone, If I must weep with Thee, "My Lord, Thy will be done."
calm-ly on, And sing, in life or death, "My Lord: Thy will be done."

No. 117. Glory to His Name.

Rev. E. A. HOFFMAN.   Rev. J. H. STOCKTON.

1. Down at the cross where my Sav-iour died, Down where for cleansing from
2. I am so won-drous-ly saved from sin! Je - sus so sweet-ly a -
3. O precious fountain that saves from sin, I am so glad I have
4. Come to this fountain, so rich and sweet: Cast thy poor soul at the

sin I cried; There to my heart was the blood ap-plied; Glo - ry to His
bides with-in; There at the cross where He took me in; Glo - ry to His
en-tered in; There Je - sus saves me and keeps me clean; Glo - ry to His
Saviour's feet; Plunge in to-day, and be made complete; Glo - ry to His

D. S.—There to my heart was the blood ap-plied ; Glo - ry to His

FINE. CHORUS.   D.S.

name! Glo - ry to His name! Glo - ry to His name!

name!

No. 118. All Hail the Power.

Rev. E. PERRONET.   OLIVER HOLDEN.

1. All hail the pow'r of Je - sus' name! Let an - gels pros-trate fall;
2. Ye chos-en seed of Is - rael's race, Ye ran-somed from the fall,
3. Let ev - 'ry kin - dred, ev - 'ry tribe, On this ter - res - trial ball,
4. O that with yon - der sa - cred throng We at His feet may fall;

Bring forth the roy - al di - a - dem, And crown Him Lord of all;
Hail Him who saves you by His grace, And crown Him Lord of all;
To Him all maj - es - ty as - cribe, And crown Him Lord of all;
We'll join the ev - er - last-ing song, And crown Him Lord of all;

Bring forth the roy - al di - a - dem, And crown Him Lord of all.
Hail Him who saves you by His grace, And crown Him Lord of all.
To Him all maj - es - ty as - cribe, And crown Him Lord of all.
We'll join the ev - er - last-ing song, And crown Him Lord of all.

No. 119.   Jesus, Saviour, Pilot Me!

Rev. EDWARD HOPPER.

J. E. GOULD.

1. Je - sus, Sav - iour, pi - lot me,   O - ver life's tem-pest-uous sea;
2. As a moth - er stills her child, Thou canst hush the o - cean wild;
3. When at last I near the shore, And the fear - ful break-ers roar

Unknown waves be - fore me roll, Hid - ing rock and treach'rous shoal;
Boist-'rous waves o - bey Thy will, When Thou say'st to them "Be still!"
Twixt me and the peace-ful rest, Then, while lean-ing on Thy breast,

Chart and com - pass come from Thee: Je - sus, Sav - iour, pi - lot me.
Won-drous Sov - 'reign of the sea, Je - sus, Sav - iour, pi - lot me.
May I hear Thee say to me, "Fear not, I will pi - lot thee!"

No. 120.   All to Christ I Owe.

ELVINA M. HALL.

JOHN T. GRAPE.

1. I hear the Saviour say— Thy strength indeed is small; Child of weakness,
2. Lord, now in-deed I find Thy pow'r, and Thine a - lone, Can change the
3. For noth-ing good have I Where - by Thy grace to claim—I'll wash my
4. When from my dy-ing bed My ransomed soul shall rise, Then "Je - sus
5. And when be-fore the throne I stand in Him complete, I'll lay my

CHORUS.

watch and pray, Find in Me thine all in all.
lep - er's spots, And melt the heart of stone.
garments white In the blood of Calv'ry's Lamb. } Je - sus paid it all!
paid it all!" Shall rend the vault - ed skies.
tro-phies down, All down a' Je - sus' feet.

All to Him I owe; Sin had left a crimson stain; He washed it white as snow.

No. 121. Come, Thou Almighty King.

CHARLES WESLEY.　　　　　　　　　　　　　FELICE GIARDINI.

1. Come, Thou almighty King, Help us Thy name to sing, Help us to praise; Father all
2. Come, Thou incarnate Word, Gird on Thy mighty sword, Our pray'r attend; Come and Thy
3. Come, ho-ly Comfort-er, Thy sacred witness bear In this glad hour: Thou who al-
4. To the great One in Three, The highest prais-es be, Hence evermore! His sov'reign

glo - ri-ous. O'er all vic-to - ri-ous, Come, and reign o-ver us, Ancient of Days.
peo-ple bless, And give Thy word success: Spirit of ho - li ness, On us de scend!
might y art, Now rule in ev-'ry heart, And ne'er from us depart, Spirit of pow'r!
ma - jes-ty May we in glo - ry see, And to e - ter - ni-ty Love and a- dore.

No. 122. My Faith Looks Up to Thee.

RAY PALMER.　　　　　　　　　　　　　LOWELL MASON.

1. My faith looks up to Thee, Thou Lamb of Cal vary, Saviour di vine; Now hear me
2. May Thy rich grace impart Strength to my fainting heart, My zeal inspire! As Thou hast

while I pray, Take all my guilt away, O let me from this day Be whol-ly Thine!
died for me, O may my love to Thee Pure, warm, and changeless be, A living fire!

3 While life's dark maze I tread,
And griefs around me spread,
　Be Thou my Guide;
Bid darkness turn to day.
Wipe sorrow's tears away,
Nor let me ever stray
　From Thee aside.

4 When ends life's transient dream,
When death's cold, sullen stream
　Shall o'er me roll;
Blest Saviour, then, in love,
Fear and distrust remove;
O bear me safe above,
　A ransomed soul!

No. 123. Happy Day.

P. DODDRIDGE.　　　　　　　　　　　　　E. F. RIMBAUDT.

1. { O hap- py day, that fix'd my choice On Thee, my Saviour and my God!
Well may this glowing heart rejoice, And tell its rap tures all a-broad. } Happy

Happy Day.—Concluded.

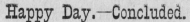

FINE.   D.S.

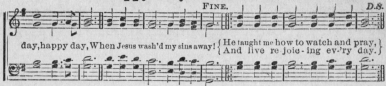

day, happy day, When Jesus wash'd my sins away! { He taught me how to watch and pray, / And live re joic-ing ev'ry day. }

2 O happy bond, that seals my vows
To Him who merits all my love!
Let cheerful anthems fill His house,
While to that sacred shrine I move.

3 'Tis done: the great transaction's done!
I am my Lord's and He is mine;
He drew me, and I followed on,
Charmed to confess the voice divine.

No. 124.   Revive us Again.

WM. P. MACKAY.   J. J. HUSBAND.

1. We praise Thee, O God! for the Son of Thy love, For Jesus who died, and is now gone above.

CHORUS.

Hal-le-lu-jah! Thine the glory, Hal-le-lu-jah! A-men, Re-vive us a-gain.

2 We praise Thee, O God! for Thy Spirit of light,
Who has shown us our Saviour, and scattered our night.

3 All glory and praise to the Lamb that was slain,
Who has borne all our sins, and has cleansed every stain.

4 All glory and praise to the God of all grace,
Who has bought us, and sought us, and guided our ways.

5 Revive us again; fill each heart with Thy love;
May each soul be rekindled with fire from above.

No. 125.   My Country! 'Tis of Thee.

S. F. SMITH, D. D.   Ad. HENRY CAREY.

1. My country! 'tis of thee, Sweet land of lib-er-ty, Of thee I sing: Land where my
2. My na-tive country thee, Land of the no-ble free, Thy name I love; I love thy

fathers died! Land of the Pilgrim's pride! From every mountain side, Let freedom ring.
rocks and rills, Thy woods and templed hills; My heart with rapture thrills, Like that above.

3 Let music swell the breeze,
And ring from all the trees
Sweet freedom's song;
Let mortal tongues awake;
Let all that breathe partake;
Let rocks their silence break,
The sound prolong.

4 Our fathers' God! to Thee,
Author of liberty,
To Thee we sing;
Long may our land be bright
With freedom's holy light;
Protect us by Thy might,
Great God, our King!

No. 126.   Pass Me Not.

FANNY J. CROSBY.
                                       W. H. DOANE.

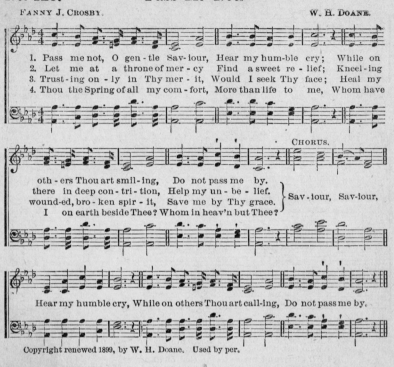

1. Pass me not, O gen-tle Sav-iour, Hear my hum-ble cry; While on
2. Let me at a throne of mer-cy Find a sweet re-lief; Kneel-ing
3. Trust-ing on-ly in Thy mer-it, Would I seek Thy face; Heal my
4. Thou the Spring of all my com-fort, More than life to me, Whom have

CHORUS.

oth-ers Thou art smil-ing, Do not pass me by.
there in deep con-tri-tion, Help my un-be-lief.
wound-ed, bro-ken spir-it, Save me by Thy grace.
I on earth beside Thee? Whom in heav'n but Thee?
       } Sav-iour, Sav-iour,

Hear my humble cry, While on others Thou art call-ing, Do not pass me by.

Copyright renewed 1899, by W. H. Doane. Used by per.

No. 127.   Come, ye Sinners, Poor and Needy.

JOSEPH HART.
                                       Anon.
                                       FINE.

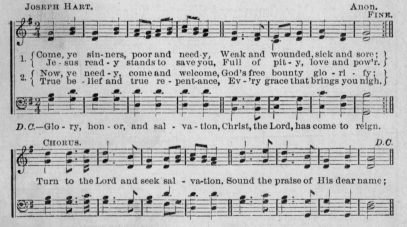

1. { Come, ye sin-ners, poor and need-y, Weak and wounded, sick and sore;
   { Je-sus read-y stands to save you, Full of pit-y, love and pow'r. }
2. { Now, ye need-y, come and welcome, God's free bounty glo-ri-fy;
   { True be-lief and true re-pent-ance, Ev-'ry grace that brings you nigh. }

D.C.—Glo-ry, hon-or, and sal-va-tion, Christ, the Lord, has come to reign.

CHORUS.   D.C.

Turn to the Lord and seek sal-va-tion, Sound the praise of His dear name;

3 Let not conscience make you linger,
    Or of fitness fondly dream;
    All the fitness He requireth,
    Is to feel your need of Him.

4 Come, ye weary, heavy laden,
    Bruised and mangled by the fall.
    If you tarry till you're better,
    You will never come at all.

No. 128.   Abide With Me.

Rev. H. F. LYTE.   WM. H. MONK

1. A - bide with me; fast falls the e - ven - tide; The dark - ness
2. Swift to its close ebbs out life's lit - tle day; Earth's joys grow
3. I need Thy pres - ence ev - 'ry pass - ing hour: What but Thy
4. Hold Thou Thy cross be - fore my clos - ing eyes; Shine thro' the

deep - ens; Lord, with me a - bide: When oth - er help - ers
dim, its glo - ries pass a - way, Change and de - cay in
grace can foil the tempter's pow'r? Who, like Thy - self my
gloom, and point me to the skies; Heav'n's morn - ing breaks, and

fail, and com-forts flee, Help of the help-less, oh, a - bide with me!
all a round I see; O Thou, who changest not, a - bide with me!
guide and stay can be? Thro' cloud and sunshine, oh, a - bide with me!
earth's vain shadows flee; In life, in death, O Lord, a - bide with me!

No. 129.   Rock of Ages.

Rev. A. M. TOPLADY   Dr. THOS. HASTINGS.

1. Rock of A - ges, cleft for me, Let me hide my - self in Thee;
2. Could my tears for - ev - er flow, Could my zeal no languor know,
3. While I draw this fleet-ing breath, When my eyes shall close in death,

Let the wa - ter and the blood, From Thy wound-ed side which flow'd,
These for sin could not a - tone; Thou must save, and Thou a - lone:
When I rise to worlds un-known, And be - hold Thee on Thy throne,

Be of sin the doub - le cure, Save from wrath and make me pure.
In my hand no price I bring; Sim - ply to Thy cross I cling.
Rock of A - ges, cleft for me, Let me hide my - self in Thee.

No. 130. Jesus, Lover of My Soul.

CHARLES WESLEY.   JOS. P. HOLBROOK.

1. Je - sus, Lov - er of my soul, Let me to Thy bos - om fly,
2. Oth - er ref - uge have I none, Hangs my help-less soul on Thee;
3. Thou, O Christ, art all I want; More than all in Thee I find;
4. Plenteous grace with Thee is found—Grace to cov - er all my sin;

While the near - er wa - ters roll, While the tem - pest still is high:
Leave, oh, leave me not a - lone, Still sup - port and comfort me;
Raise the fall - en, cheer the faint, Heal the sick, and lead the blind:
Let the heal-ing streams a - bound; Make me, keep me, pure with-in,

Hide me, oh, my Sav - iour, hide, Till the storm of life is past;
All my trust on Thee is stayed, All my help from Thee I bring;
Just and ho - ly is Thy name, I am all un-right-eous ness;
Thou of life the Fountain art, Free - ly let me take of Thee;

Safe in - to the ha - ven guide, Oh, re - ceive my soul at last.
Cov - er my de - fence-less head With the shad - ow of Thy wing.
Vile and full of sin I am, Thou art full of truth and grace.
Spring Thou up with-in my heart, Rise to all e - ter - ni - ty.

Used by permission.

Jesus, Lover of My Soul.

CHARLES WESLEY.   (SECOND TUNE.)   SIMEON B. MARSH.
                                             FINE.

1. { Je - sus, Lov - er of my soul, Let me to Thy bos - om fly, }
{ While the near - er wa - ters roll, While the tem - pest still is high; }

D.C.—Safe in - to the ha - ven guide, Oh, re ceive my soul at last.

                                                D.C.

Hide me, oh, my Sav - iour, hide, Till the storm of life is past;

No. 131. From All that Dwell Below the Skies.

ISAAC WATTS.   JOHN HATTON.

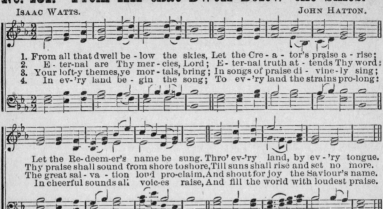

1. From all that dwell be - low the skies, Let the Cre - a - tor's praise a - rise;
2. E - ter-nal are Thy mer - cies, Lord; E - ter-nal truth at - tends Thy word;
3. Your loft-y themes, ye mor - tals, bring; In songs of praise di - vine-ly sing;
4. In ev-'ry land be - gin the song; To ev-'ry land the strains pro-long:

Let the Re - deem-er's name be sung. Thro' ev-'ry land, by ev - 'ry tongue.
Thy praise shall sound from shore to shore, Till suns shall rise and set no more.
The great sal - va - tion loud pro-claim, And shout for joy the Saviour's name.
In cheerful sounds all voic-es raise, And fill the world with loudest praise.

No. 132. SING TO THE LORD.

1 All people that on earth do dwell,
  Sing to the Lord with cheerful voice:
  Him serve with fear, His praise forth tell,
  Come ye before Him, and rejoice.

2 The Lord, ye know is God indeed,
  Without our aid He did us make;
  We are His flock, He doth us feed,
  And for His sheep He doth us take.

3 O enter then His gates with praise,
  Approach with joy His courts unto:
  Praise, laud, and bless His name always,
  For it is seemly so to do.

4 For why? the Lord our God is good,
  His mercy is forever sure;
  His truth at all times firmly stood;
  And shall from age to age endure.
                              WILLIAM KETHE.

No. 133. When I Survey the Wondrous Cross.

ISAAC WATTS   ISAAC BAKER WOODBURY.

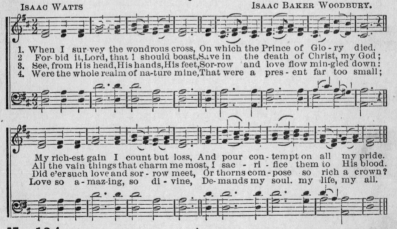

1. When I sur-vey the wondrous cross, On which the Prince of Glo-ry died,
2. For-bid it, Lord, that I should boast, Save in the death of Christ, my God;
3. See, from His head, His hands, His feet, Sor-row and love flow min-gled down:
4. Were the whole realm of na-ture mine, That were a pres-ent far too small;

My rich-est gain I count but loss, And pour con-tempt on all my pride.
All the vain things that charm me most, I sac - ri - fice them to His blood.
Did e'er such love and sor - row meet, Or thorns com-pose so rich a crown?
Love so a-maz-ing, so di - vine, De-mands my soul, my life, my all.

No. 134. JESUS SHALL REIGN.

1 Jesus shall reign where'er the sun
  Does his successive journeys run;
  His kingdom spread from shore to shore,
  Till moons shall wax and wane no more.

2 From north to south the princes meet,
  To pay their homage at His feet;
  While western empires own their Lord,
  And savage tribes attend His word.

3 To Him shall endless prayer be made,
  And endless praises crown His head;
  His name like sweet perfume shall rise
  With every morning sacrifice.

4 People and realms of every tongue
  Dwell on His love with sweetest song,
  And infant voices shall proclaim
  Their early blessings on His name.
                              ISAAC WATTS.

No. 135. Whiter than Snow.

JAMES NICHOLSON.   WM. G. FISCHER.

1. Lord Je-sus, I long to be per-fect-ly whole; I want Thee for-ev-er to
2. Lord Je-sus, look down from Thy throne in the skies, And help me to make a com-
3. Lord Je-sus, for this I most humbly en-treat; I wait, blessed Lord, at Thy
4. Lord Je-sus, Thou se-est I pa-tient-ly wait; Come now, and within me a

live in my soul; Break down ev-'ry i - dol, cast out ev-'ry foe;
plete sac-ri-fice; I give up my-self, and what-ev-er I know;
cru-ci-fied feet, By faith, for my cleansing, I see Thy blood flow!
new heart cre-ate; To those who have sought Thee, Thou never said'st "No,"

CHORUS.

Now wash me, and I shall be whit-er than snow. Whit-er than snow, yes,

whit-er than snow; Now wash me, and I shall be whit-er than snow.

Copyright, 1871, by Wm. G. Fischer. Used by per.

No. 136. Only Trust Him.

J. H. S.   Rev. J. H. STOCKTON.

1. Come, ev-'ry soul by sin oppressed, There's mercy with the Lord, And He will sure-ly
2. For Je-sus shed His pre-cious blood Rich blessings to be-stow: Plunge now in-to the
3. Yes, Je-sus is the Truth, the Way, That leads you in-to rest; Be-lieve in Him with
4. Come, then, and join this ho-ly band, And on to glo-ry go, To dwell in that ce-

D.S.—He will save you,

FINE. CHORUS.   D.S.

give you rest, By trust-ing in His word,
crim-son flood That washes white as snow.
out de-lay, And you are ful-ly blest.
les-tial land, Where joys immortal flow.

On-ly trust Him, only trust Him, Only trust Him now:

He will save you, He will save you now.

No. 137. How Firm a Foundation.

G. KEITH.

M. PORTOGALLO.

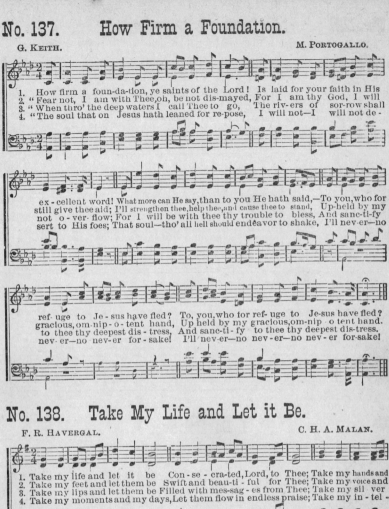

1. How firm a foun-da-tion, ye saints of the Lord! Is laid for your faith in His
2. "Fear not, I am with Thee, oh, be not dis-mayed, For I am thy God, I will
3. "When thro' the deep waters I call Thee to go, The riv-ers of sor-row shall
4. "The soul that on Jesus hath leaned for re-pose, I will not—I will not de-

ex - cellent word! What more can He say, than to you He hath said,—To you, who for
still give thee aid; I'll strengthen thee, help thee, and cause thee to stand, Up-held by my
not o - ver- flow; For I will be with thee thy trouble to bless, And sanc-ti-fy
sert to His foes; That soul—tho' all hell should endeavor to shake, I'll nev-er—no

ref· uge to Je - sus have fled? To, you, who for ref- uge to Je-sus have fled?
gracious, om-nip - o - tent hand, Up held by my gracious, om-nip o tent hand.
to thee thy deepest dis - tress, And sanc-ti- fy to thee thy deepest dis-tress.
nev· er—no nev-er for - sake! I'll nev-er—no nev-er—no nev-er for-sake!

No. 138. Take My Life and Let it Be.

F. R. HAVERGAL.

C. H. A. MALAN.

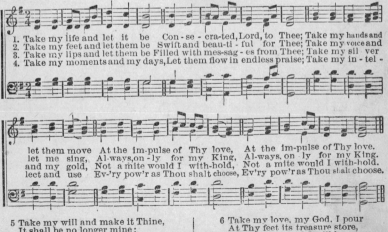

1. Take my life and let it be Con - se - cra-ted, Lord, to Thee; Take my hands and
2. Take my feet and let them be Swift and beau-ti - ful for Thee; Take my voice and
3. Take my lips and let them be Filled with mes-sag - es from Thee; Take my sil ver
4. Take my moments and my days, Let them flow in endless praise; Take my in - tel -

let them move At the im-pulse of Thy love, At the im-pulse of Thy love.
let me sing, Al-ways, on -ly for my King, Al-ways, on ly for my King.
and my gold, Not a mite would I with-hold, Not a mite would I with-hold.
lect and use Ev'ry pow'r as Thou shalt choose, Ev'ry pow'r as Thou shalt choose.

5 Take my will and make it Thine,
It shall be no longer mine;
Take my heart, it is Thine own,
It shall be Thy royal throne,
It shall be Thy royal throne.

6 Take my love, my God, I pour
At Thy feet its treasure store,
Take myself, and I will be
Ever, only, all for Thee,
Ever, only, all for Thee.

No. 139. My Jesus, I Love Thee.

London Hymn Book.

A. J. Gordon.

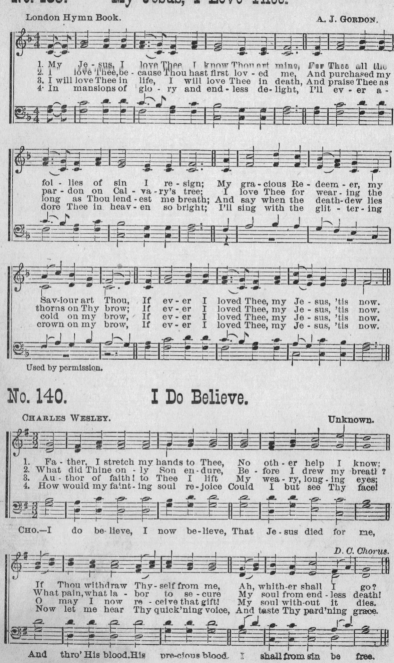

1. My Jesus, I love Thee, I know Thou art mine, For Thee all the
2. I love Thee, be-cause Thou hast first lov-ed me, And purchased my
3. I will love Thee in life, I will love Thee in death, And praise Thee as
4. In mansions of glo-ry and end-less de-light, I'll ev-er a-

fol-lies of sin I re-sign; My gra-cious Re-deem-er, my
par-don on Cal-va-ry's tree; I love Thee for wear-ing the
long as Thou lend-est me breath; And say when the death-dew lies
dore Thee in heav-en so bright; I'll sing with the glit-ter-ing

Sav-iour art Thou, If ev-er I loved Thee, my Je-sus, 'tis now.
thorns on Thy brow; If ev-er I loved Thee, my Je-sus, 'tis now.
cold on my brow, If ev-er I loved Thee, my Je-sus, 'tis now.
crown on my brow, If ev-er I loved Thee, my Je-sus, 'tis now.

Used by permission.

No. 140. I Do Believe.

Charles Wesley.

Unknown.

1. Fa-ther, I stretch my hands to Thee, No oth-er help I know;
2. What did Thine on-ly Son en-dure, Be-fore I drew my breath?
3. Au-thor of faith! to Thee I lift My wea-ry, long-ing eyes;
4. How would my faint-ing soul re-joice Could I but see Thy face!

Cho.—I do be-lieve, I now be-lieve, That Je-sus died for me,

D. C. Chorus.

If Thou withdraw Thy-self from me, Ah, whith-er shall I go?
What pain, what la-bor to se-cure My soul from end-less death!
O may I now re-ceive that gift! My soul with-out it dies.
Now let me hear Thy quick'ning voice, And taste Thy pard'ning grace.

And thro' His blood, His pre-cious blood, I shall from sin be free,

Walk in the Light.

B. BARTON.

From MEHUL and HAYDN.

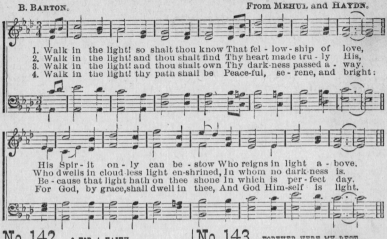

1. Walk in the light! so shalt thou know That fel - low - ship of love,
2. Walk in the light! and thou shalt find Thy heart made tru - ly His,
3. Walk in the light! and thou shalt own Thy dark-ness passed a - way.
4. Walk in the light! thy path shall be Peace-ful, se - rene, and bright:

His Spir - it on - ly can be - stow Who reigns in light a - bove.
Who dwells in cloud-less light en-shrined, In whom no dark-ness is.
Be - cause that light hath on thee shone In which is per - fect day.
For God, by grace, shall dwell in thee, And God Him-self is light.

No. 142. O FOR A FAITH.

1 O for a faith that will not shrink,
  Though pressed by every foe,
  That will not tremble on the brink
  Of any earthly woe!

2 That will not murmur nor complain
  Beneath the chastening rod,
  But, in the hour of grief and pain,
  Will lean upon its God;

3 A faith that shines more bright and clear,
  When tempests rage without;
  That when in danger knows no fear,
  In darkness feels no doubt;

4 Lord, give us such a faith as this,
  And then, whate'er may come,
  We'll taste, e'en here, the hallowed bliss
  Of an eternal home.
  WILLIAM HILEY BATHURST.

No. 143. FOREVER HERE MY REST.

1 Forever here my rest shall be
  Close to Thy bleeding side;
  This all my hope, and all my plea,
  For me the Saviour died.

2 My dying Saviour and my God,
  Fountain for guilt and sin,
  Sprinkle me ever with Thy blood,
  And cleanse and keep me clean.

3 Wash me, and make me thus Thine own;
  Wash me, and mine Thou art;
  Wash me, but not my feet alone,—
  My hands, my head, my heart.

4 Th'atonement o Thy blood apply
  Till a signt improve;
  Till hope in full fruition die,
  And all my soul be love
  CHARLES WESLEY.

Azmon.

C. G. GLASER.

No. 144. O FOR A THOUSAND TONGUES!

1 O for a thousand tongues, to sing
  My great Redeemer's praise;
  The glories of my God and King,
  The triumphs of His grace!

2 My gracious Master and my God,
  Assist me to proclaim,
  To spread through all the earth abroad,
  The honors of Thy name.

3 Jesus! the name that charms our fears,
  That bids our sorrows cease;
  'Tis music in the sinner's ears,
  'Tis life, and health, and peace.

4 He breaks the power of canceled sin,
  He sets the prisoner free;
  His blood can make the foulest clean;
  His blood availed for me.
  CHARLES WESLEY.

No. 145. O FOR A HEART TO PRAISE.

1 O for a heart to praise my God,
  A heart from sin set free!
  A heart that always feels Thy blood,
  So freely spilt for me!

2 A heart resigned, submissive, meek,
  My great Redeemer's throne;
  Where only Christ is heard to speak,
  Where Jesus reigns alone.

3 O for a lowly, contrite heart,
  Believing, true, and clean,
  Which neither life nor death can part
  From Him that dwells within!

4 A heart in every thought renewed,
  And full of love divine;
  Perfect, and right, and pure, and good,
  A copy, Lord, of Thine.
  CHARLES WESLEY.

INDEX.

	No.
Abiding in Christ	93
Abide with Me	128
All Hail the Power	118
All to Christ I Owe	120
All the Way My Saviour	15
Anywhere With Jesus	21
At the Cross	49
Battle Hymn of	91
Beautiful Robes	104
Blessed Assurance	75
Blessed Jesus Keep Me	80
Blessings	50
Blest be the Tie	33
Come, Thou Almighty K	121
Come, Ye Sinners	127
Day is Dying in	107
Dear to the Heart	10
Does Jesus Care	6
Drifting Down	18
Draw Me Nearer	55
Every Day and Hour	33
Even Me	35
Face to Face	99
Fill Me Now	73
Forever Here My Rest	143
From All that Dwell	131
Full of Free Sal	36
Give Me Jesus	19
Glory All the Way	23
Glory to His Name	117
God Be With You	110
Happy Day	123
He's Always Good	32
He's Everything to	103
Heavenly Sunlight	74
Help Just a Little	2
He Hideth My Soul	81
Hide Thou Me	11
Higher Ground	3
His Way with Thee	37
How Firm a Foundation	137
I Cannot Let Him Go	29
I Do Believe	140
I Have Found a Friend	96
I Know He's Mine	94
I Know that My R	13
I Must Tell Jesus	41

	No.
I Need Thee Every H	105
I Remember Calvary	1
I Shall L. Like Hi.	8
I'll go Where You	52
I'll Follow Where He	7
Is Thy Heart Right	45
It is Well With my	43
It was Spoken for	42
Jesus, I Come	24
Jesus is all the World	56
Jesus is Passing	72
Jesus, Lover of My	130
Jesus, Saves	57
Jesus Shall Reign	134
Jesus, Saviour Pilot	119
Just as I Am	111
Keep On the Sunny	89
Labor On	87
Lead and Keep Me	64
Lead Me, Saviour	97
Leaning on the Everlast	58
Let Jesus Come Into	20
Love Divine	63
Make Me a Blessing	5
More and More	76
More Love to Thee	53
My Country 'Tis	125
My Jesus, I Love	139
My Jesus, As Thou	116
My Faith Looks Up	122
My Mother is Praying	109
My Redeemer	70
My Saviour First	9
My Saviour is With Me	106
My Soul is Anchored	101
Nearer the Cross	31
Nearer, My God, to Thee	69
Never Alone	98
No, Not One	71
O For a Faith	142
O For a Thousand T	144
O For a Heart	145
O Think of a Home	95
Oh, 'Tis Glory	39
One More Day's Work	88
Only Trust Him	136
Onward, Christian Sol	77
Open Wide the Door	22

	No.
Patiently Pleading	48
Pass Me Not	126
Peace Through the B	28
Precious Name	79
Ready to Do	51
Revive us Again	124
Rock of Ages	129
Saved by Grace	67
Seeking the Lost	68
Seek Ye First the	84
Sing On	82
Sing to the Lord	132
Softly and Tenderly	65
Speed for Thy Life	47
Standing on the P	17
Stepping in the Light	108
Sunshine in the S	61
Sweet Peace, the Gift	16
Take My Life and L	138
Tell the Sweet Story	30
The Call for Reapers	112
The Glad Reunion	102
The Grand Old Story	44
The Half was Never T	4
The Saviour Precious	59
The Stranger at the	60
The Shepherd Calls	26
There is Power in t	27
There Shall be Showers	92
There is a Fountain	113
There's a Wideness	114
The Story that N	85
Thou Canst Save	46
Trust and Obey	86
'Tis So Sweet to T	78
Walk Beside Me	66
Walk in the Light	141
We Have An Anchor	25
We're Marching to Z	100
Whiter than Snow	135
When I Stand on the S	54
When Love Shines In	34
When the Bridegroom C	12
When I Survey T	133
Winning Precious Souls	38
Will there Be any S	14
Wilt Thou Be made W	90
Wonderful Story of	62
Work for the Night	115
Wonderful Peace	40